Experiments in microbial genetics

Edited by
R. C. Clowes
B.Sc. Ph.D. D.Sc.
Professor, Division of Biology
Southwest Center for Advanced Studies
Dallas, Texas

and
W. Hayes
D.Sc. F.R.S.
Professor of Molecular Genetics,
University of Edinburgh, and
Honorary Director of the Medical
Research Council's Microbial Genetics Research
Unit, Department of Molecular Biology,
University of Edinburgh

John Wiley & Sons Inc
New York

Printed in Great Britain

Table of contents

v   143195

Contents

Contents

vii

Contents

Contents

Appendices

Contributors

The experiments were presented in practical classes and prepared for this book by the following authors. The experiments for which each is responsible are shown at the left.

19,20,21,22,24, 25,26,27	**R.C.Clowes** B.Sc. Ph.D. D.Sc. *Professor, Division of Biology, Southwest Center for Advanced Studies, Dallas, Texas*
4,5,6,11,12	**K.W.Fisher** B.Sc. Ph.D. *Division of Biology, Kansas State University, Manhattan, Kansas*
1,2,3	**S.W.Glover** B.Sc. Ph.D. *Medical Research Council's Microbial Genetics Research Unit, Department of Molecular Biology, University of Edinburgh*
28,29,30,31,32	**W.Hayes** D.Sc. F.R.S. *Professor of Molecular Genetics, University of Edinburgh*
33,34,35,36,37	**R.H.Pritchard** B.Sc. Ph.D. *Professor of Genetics, University of Leicester*
7,8,9,10	**K.A.Stacey** Ph.D. *Department of Biological Sciences, University of Sussex*
13,14,15,16,17, 18,23	**N.Symonds** B.A. B.Sc. Ph.D. *Professor of Microbial Genetics, University of Sussex*

Preface

During the summer months of 1960, 1961, 1962 and 1964, a four-week practical course in microbial genetics was presented by the members of the staff of the Medical Research Council's Microbial Genetics Research Unit at Hammersmith Hospital, London. Many of the staff members had experienced and enjoyed the excellent summer courses in phage and bacterial genetics that had been presented at Cold Spring Harbor, New York, and so were encouraged to present their own specialities in a similar practical course. Each course was attended by 18–24 students drawn from universities and research departments mainly in the United Kingdom, but extending to nine other European countries. Those attending ranged in experience from professor to post-graduate student and came from such diverse backgrounds as bacteriology, biochemistry, genetics, physics and virology. The course was primarily 'do-it-yourself', designed around 30 or more key experiments in microbial genetics, one or two experiments being performed per day. The experiments were supplemented by about 40 or so lectures and tutorials which attempted to cover some of the more theoretical aspects of molecular biology. The success of these courses, the considerable demand for copies of the experimental notes and the dispersion of many of those involved in the teaching has prompted us to present the laboratory material in this published form.

The experiments represent the personal choices of the individual instructors and reflect their own compromises for those that demonstrate certain basic concepts in modern genetics, whilst being capable of giving clear and reproducible results in a minimum of time by the inexperienced experimentalist. It is to be hoped that these experiments, although by no means giving an exhaustive coverage of microbial genetics, will help to fill the gap which confronts those instructors, who, although familiar with the published literature, are hesitant to attempt to reproduce the supporting experiments with a class of students.

The experiments

Except for the section on Aspergillus, the experiments are arranged in the order in which they were performed during the series of practical courses, so that students with no previous experience of working with microorganisms, or of sterile techniques, may acquire the necessary experience during the first few experiments.

However, since some of the experiments with Aspergillus require many days for incubation, they were usually initiated after the virulent phage experiments, and terminated during the period when the experiments on transduction and conjugation were presented.

As a rule, each experiment is dealt with under five general headings.

Background. A short discussion of the field of study. When several successive experiments deal with related aspects (for example, experiments 13 to 18 with virulent 'T' phages), this section may be common to a group of experiments. A list of relevant references is given at the end of this section.

Intention of what the experiment is designed to illustrate. In this section is also included any pre-preparations that are necessary in order to provide the starting materials (for example: preparation of DNA and phage suspensions).

Requirements. These are based upon the needs of each experimenter, or small group of individuals working together, and include details of small apparatus, media, and cultures that are required for each independent step of the experiment. The microbial stocks necessary for each experiment will be listed serially throughout the text (prefaced by 'EMG'). A key is provided in Appendix B, which specifies the stock used in past courses and lists alternative stocks which may serve as substitutes. (However, use of alternative strains may in some instances require minor modifications in the experimental procedures.) Appendix B also gives the addresses of those British and American Culture Collections from which the specified strains may be obtained at the normal fee. Appendix C provides a list of addresses at which various strains of microorganisms may be available.

Methods. In this section, the detailed day-to-day operations are set out with approximate times required for each operation and the optimal periods required between successive operations. Here the actual methods used to obtain reproducible results are noted, although variations in techniques and apparatus can often be satisfactorily substituted. Where possible, alternative techniques have been indicated.

Conclusions. This part includes a discussion of the results the student should expect and leads him to draw the correct conclusions from the experiment.

General Notes

To avoid repetition, the words 'sterile' and 'sterilization' have been omitted from most of the text. It should be assumed that all solutions and glassware used in each experiment are sterile. Moreover, although for most experiments it is not necessary to observe complete sterility, reasonable precautions should be taken, *i.e.*, bottles and tubes should remain uncapped and the agar surfaces of plates should remain exposed for minimal periods. In addition, an incubation temperature of 37°C should be used throughout, unless otherwise stated. All temperatures are expressed in degrees *centigrade*, shown without C.

Genetic loci are usually shown as 3-letter italic symbols [as recently proposed by Demerec *et al.* (1966) *Genetics*, **54**, 61]. For example, *met⁻* indicates a methionine-requiring strain (see Appendix B for abbreviations). The growth-factor requirements of strains are often abbreviated as similar 3-letter roman symbols; e.g. Minimal Medium supplemented with methionine is often abbreviated as MM + met (see Appendix A).

General methods and techniques

1. Media Preparation and Plate Pouring

The composition of the various media are detailed in Appendix A (pp. 184 to 192). Solid constituents of media may conveniently be dissolved and made up to volume in bulk quantities, dispensed in screw-capped (s/c) bottles (see p. 11) and sterilized by steam under pressure.* (IMPORTANT: screw-caps should be loosened before pressure is applied. They are tightened on cooling, and the sterile media can then be stored in this condition for indefinite periods at room temperature.)

To pour 'plates', agar medium, if taken from store, is melted by a short exposure to steam pressure at 15 pounds per square inch (lb.psi) and, where necessary, the other pre-warmed ingredients are added. The medium (at about 70°) is then dispensed into petri dishes (about 25 ml for growth of micro-organisms as separate colonies, or about 40 ml for phage and other experiments, when confluent growth of micro-organisms as a 'lawn' is required). Bubbles are removed by bunsen-burner flame. The dish lids are then replaced leaving a small vent until the agar has set. Excess condensation is removed (the plates are 'dried') by incubating the plates upside-down, and with the lids off, in a warm room for about an hour at 37°. Alternatively, they can be dried by incubation overnight in the inverted position but with the lids on. Most problems arising from contamination may be avoided if plates (particularly those used in 'spreading' techniques) are used the same day, or no more than one day, after pouring, storing for short periods if necessary in a refrigerator or cold room.

2. Preservation of bacterial cultures

Stock cultures of bacterial strains are preserved as *stabs* in 'stab' medium (Appendix A22) in small, tightly-capped tubes which can be hermetically sealed as, for example, by a plastic stopper,† kept at room temperature in

---

* Media can alternatively be made up in large Erlenmayer flasks and used at once, or capped with foil and stored for limited periods.
† e.g. ½ dram vials, Camlab (Glass) Cambridge are suitable.

the dark. From these master cultures, *nutrient agar slopes* (Appendix A21) are inoculated and single colonies of the strains isolated from these by streaking on plates of nutrient agar (*stock plate*).*

3. Preparation of liquid-grown bacterial cultures

(a) 'Overnight' Cultures

For many experiments, the starting material is an overnight (o/n) bacterial culture. An inoculum from a single colony on the stock plate is taken into fluid medium† and incubated without aeration overnight (for about 18 hr at 37°), when the concentration of cells will usually have reached about 10^9 organisms per ml.

(b) *Exponential or logarithmically-growing (log.) cultures*

From an o/n culture, a dilution is made into fresh medium and aerated at 37° to achieve a cell density of approximately 2×10^8/ml. Two techniques are commonly employed. The culture may be diluted into a s/c bottle and incubated on a 33 rpm rotor (see p. 10), a 1 in 10 dilution requiring about $1\frac{1}{2}$ hr in broth, and 1 in 50 dilution about $2\frac{1}{2}$ hr. Alternatively, the culture can be diluted into a 'bubbler' tube (see p. 11) and aerated by bubbling air from an aeration pump (see p. 10), this method being a little more efficient. Here again, the use of s/c bottles permit subsequent centrifugation without transferring to a centrifuge tube.

4. Streaking for single colonies

A sterile wire loop dipped into a bacterial culture, or touched on a bacterial colony, is rubbed several times across the surface of part of a plate of solid medium (Fig. 1A). The wire is sterilized by flaming and when cool, it is drawn half a dozen times at right angles across the original streaks (*B*). It is again sterilized and the cross-streaks repeated at *C* and again at *D*. After appropriate incubation of the plate (with the agar layer uppermost, to avoid condensation) (18 hr at 37° for most strains on

---

* Some workers prefer to take their inoculum direct from a slope or slant, without recourse to the intermediate stock plate. The stock plate method, however, has the advantage that the purity of the original culture may be seen from the uniformity in the morphology of the colonies and moreover any contamination of this plate is more readily noticed.

† For most experiments, an inoculum is conveniently made into 5 ml broth in a $\frac{1}{2}$ oz screw-capped bottle. This method has the advantage that the culture can then be centrifuged at low speeds (3000 rpm) in the same bottle if the cells require washing, and may then be resuspended in a different medium.

nutrient agar and 24 hr on minimal agar), growth of the individual cells will give rise to independent colonies of several mm diameter (usually in *D*, if the original inoculum was dense).

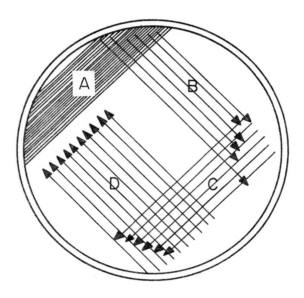

Fig. 1 Streaking a plate for single colonies of bacteria

5. Dilutions

Most bacterial cultures and phage suspensions are used at high concentrations (bacteria, 10^8 to 10^9 cells/ml; phages, 10^7 to 10^{11} particles/ml). To count the individual cells (by their ability to form colonies), or the individual phage particles (by their ability to form plaques), considerable dilution is usually necessary. This is conveniently achieved by a series of small dilutions (either tenfold or hundredfold); for example, a 1 in a million (10^{-6}) dilution is obtained by three successive 1 in 100 (10^{-2}) dilutions. Each dilution is performed by transferring 0.1 ml by sterile pipette into 10 ml of sterile liquid in a sterile tube; after swirling to mix, a *fresh*, sterile pipette is used for the next dilution.

Standard dilutions may be achieved as follows:

$$\left(\frac{0.1}{0.9} \text{ indicates 0.1 ml into 0.9 ml}\right)$$

$$10^{-1} = \frac{0.1}{0.9} \qquad\qquad 10^{-4} = \frac{0.1}{10} \times \frac{0.1}{10} \qquad\qquad 10^{-7} = \frac{0.1}{10} \times \frac{0.1}{10} \times \frac{0.1}{10} \times \frac{1}{9}$$

$$10^{-2} = \frac{0.1}{10} \qquad\qquad 10^{-5} = \frac{0.1}{10} \times \frac{0.1}{10} \times \frac{1}{9} \qquad 10^{-8} = \frac{0.1}{10} \times \frac{0.1}{10} \times \frac{0.1}{10} \times \frac{0.1}{10}$$

$$10^{-3} = \frac{0.1}{10} \times \frac{1}{9} \qquad 10^{-6} = \frac{0.1}{10} \times \frac{0.1}{10} \times \frac{0.1}{10} \qquad 10^{-9} = \frac{0.1}{10} \times \frac{0.1}{10} \times \frac{0.1}{10} \times \frac{0.1}{10} \times \frac{1}{9}$$

Dilutions are made in buffer (Appendix A14) unless otherwise stated.

6. Assay of bacterial cells or phage particles

(a) *'Total' bacterial cells ('total count')*
The number of bacteria (living or dead), present in suspensions with cell densities greater than 10^7/ml can be counted by the use of a counting chamber (Helber or Petroff-Hauser; see p. 238) viewed by dark-field or phase-contrast microscopy. All the cells in the culture, whether viable or not, are counted by this technique.

(b) *Colony-forming bacteria ('viable count')*
A liquid culture is diluted so that its cell density is about 1 to 5×10^3/ml. Samples of 0.1 ml are then assayed:
   (i) *By spreading*. A 0.1 ml drop is placed by pipette on an agar plate and spread over the surface using a bent glass rod (a 1 inch right-angled bend on a 3mm diam. glass rod) which is pre-sterilized by flaming after immersion in alcohol; after 18 hr incubation, each viable cell will produce a colony.
   (ii) *By overlay*. The 0.1 ml sample is added to 2.5 ml of soft agar (Appendix A11) in a small tube, held molten at 46° in a waterbath. The whole contents of the tube are then poured on an agar plate, which is rocked to distribute as a thin layer over the entire surface. Thin disc-like colonies are produced within the soft agar overlay which may be counted after 24 hr incubation.

(c) *Standard assay for bacteriophage*
The most widely used method for assaying phage stocks is the agar-layer method. A small volume (0.05–0.5 ml) of a diluted phage suspension is pipetted into a small tube, containing 2.5 ml of molten 'soft' agar

and about 2×10^8 bacteria which are sensitive to the phage (*indicator bacteria*). These *indicator* bacteria are conveniently added as 3–4 drops from an o/n broth culture using a 1 ml pipette or, if large numbers of overlays are required, by using the culture in a 'dropping bottle'. The agar is maintained in the molten state by holding the tube in a 46° waterbath. The mixture of phage, indicator bacteria and soft agar is then poured over the surface of a nutrient agar plate (i.e. 'plated'), and the plate is gently rocked to distribute the mixture evenly over the surface as a thin layer (overlay). When the top layer has solidified (10–15 min), the plate is inverted and placed in an incubator at 37° and incubated overnight. The next day, a continuous lawn of bacterial growth will be seen over the surface of the agar, except where a clone of phage particles has lysed the bacteria, and produced a visible, clear area or 'plaque'.

It has been shown that a single phage particle will produce a plaque. The number of plaques, therefore, gives a direct assay of the number of phage particles put on the plate. The titre of a phage preparation can then be expressed as a concentration of 'plaque-forming units' (pfu.). In the case of T phages, this is equivalent to the concentration of phage particles.

7. Preparation of phage lysates

(a) *Liquid lysates* (*of virulent phages, e.g. 'T' phages*)

About 20 ml of phage-broth (Appendix A15)* in a bubbler tube is inoculated with 0.2 ml of an o/n broth culture of the bacterial host strain and aerated by bubbling at 37° in a waterbath for about $2\frac{1}{2}$ hr, until a concentration of about 1×10^8 cells/ml is reached. Phage is then added at a concentration of 10^9 particles/ml, so that all bacteria are infected.† Aeration is continued for two to three hours when the turbid culture will often 'clear' and a final titre of 10^{10} to 10^{11} phage particles/ml will usually be achieved. Several drops of chloroform are then added, the lysate is well shaken, allowed to stand for 10 min and then decanted. It is then spun at low speed in a small, angle centrifuge to sediment bacterial debris. For further concentration, the phage may be sedimented as a pellet, after high-speed centrifugation [12,000 g for 1 hr in the case of large, T-'even' (T2, T4, T6) phages and appropriately longer for the smaller, T-'odd' (T1, T3, T5, T7) phages], which is then taken up in a

---

* M9 medium + 0.2% casamino acids can be used as an alternative. Problems of frothing associated with bubbling are then much less (see Appendix A).

† Alternatively, inoculate a 5×10^7 cells/ml culture with a straight needle after 'stabbing' a phage plaque.

small volume of phage buffer (Appendix A17) and allowed to stand overnight. It is finally well dispersed and centrifuged at low speed to remove
the last few bacterial cells.

(b) *Liquid lysates (of temperate phages, e.g. P22)*
To a similar log. culture of the host bacteria, aerated at 37° in nutrient
broth, phage is added at a multiplicity (phage per bacterium) of about 1 in
200. Aeration is continued either for 5 hr, or until the culture shows signs
of clearing (whichever is earlier), when a titre of 10^{10} to 10^{11} pfu/ml is
usually achieved. Further purification and concentration as above, noting
that P22 is a large phage and λ much smaller. (There is frequently no
correlation between the final titre and the extent of 'clearing'.)

(c) *Soft-agar lysates (of temperate phages e.g. P1 or λ)*
To a small tube containing 2.5 ml of molten soft agar, held at 46° in a
waterbath, is added 0.1 ml of a log. culture of host bacteria [any non-
P1-lysogenic K12 strain for P1, or a C600 strain (EMG10-Appendix B)
for λ] at about 5×10^8 cells/ml and 0.1 ml of a 10^7 particles/ml preparation of the phage. The tube is overlayed on a plate containing 50 ml of
T-phage nutrient agar (TNA; Appendix A16) (containing $M/100$ Ca^{++},
in the case of phage P1 and $M/100$ Mg^{++} for phage λ). After overnight*
incubation, the plate shows confluent lysis of the host cells. The soft
agar is scraped off into 2 ml phage buffer, shaken vigorously for a few
seconds and immediately centrifuged at low speed. The supernatant is
decanted, 1 drop CHCl$_3$ is added and it is recentrifuged at low speed.
The preparation will usually contain 10^{10} to 10^{11} phage particles per ml
and can be further concentrated by high-speed centrifugation.

8. Replica plating

Plates that are to be replicated are surface-spread with a dilution of a
bacterial culture that will give 100–200 colonies per plate, avoiding the
periphery of the plate. They are then incubated for a shorter than usual
period until the well-separated colonies reach a diameter of about 1 mm.
These are the 'master plates'. A suitable block for replica plating is a No.79
rubber stopper (79 mm smaller diameter), to which a sterile disc of
nylon velveteen or other similar material† about 12 cm in diameter is

---

* With P1 lysates, an incubation time of 8–10 hr is optimal.
† 11 cm filter paper may be used, provided colonies are well-separated and few
replicas are required.

fixed, by sliding over it a ring or clip.* A master-plate is now inverted on the block and contact with the pile of the material is obtained by *light* pressure. A reference mark is made on the circumference of the plate to correspond with a similar reference mark on the replicator block. A series of sterile agar plates of appropriate media may now be 'replicated' by successive inversion on this pad and similar reference marks made on each plate. Growth is observed on these 'replicate' plates after 5 to 6 hr incubation and can be compared with the 'master' after alignment of reference marks. As a control, it is advisable to include one replicate on the same medium as the 'master'.

---

* A spring-loaded and adjustable clip, such as is used in motor vehicles for attaching water-cooling hoses ('Jubilee' clip No.4 is a suitable size) will be found adequate for this purpose.

General apparatus required

It is realized that facilities will vary extensively, but the following list of simple apparatus is compiled with a view to general economy and convenience.

Sterilization

1. *Steam sterilization* under pressure from 5 to 20 lb psi is required for media and labile materials. For large classes, an autoclave is an obvious advantage, but for most purposes a large domestic pressure cooker will serve equally well.

2. *Dry heat sterilization* is needed for pipettes, tubes and other glass and metal apparatus, and is achieved in a thermostatic oven operating up to 180° (preferably with time-switch). Exposure to 160° for 2 hr is satisfactory for most purposes.

Incubation

1. *Thermostatic waterbaths*—a minimum of two per class are required, usually operating at 37° and 46°.

2. *Thermostatic incubators*, generally operating at 37°, are required for incubation of plates. A thermostatic hot-room is an advantage for large classes, and is particularly useful for drying plates.

Aeration

1. *By bubbling* is achieved by small aquarium aerators. The piston type is more robust than the moving diaphragm type (see p. 239).

2. *By rotation* of capped bottles is sometimes more convenient. A turntable fitted with clips, inclined at 45° and circulating at 33 rpm is suitable for this purpose (see p. 238). Screw-capped bottles should be filled only

one-third of capacity to contain sufficient air for adequate growth of the culture.

Glass and other apparatus

1. *Petri dishes* of glass can with advantage be replaced with plastic, pre-sterilized disposable dishes. A $3\frac{1}{2}$ inch dish (marketed in the United Kingdom at about $1\frac{1}{2}$d. to 2d. each) is suitable for most experiments (see p. 240).

2. *Pipettes*. A selection of 0.1 ml, 1 ml, and 10 ml pipettes are required for most experiments, a maximum number of about 50×0.1 ml, 50×1 ml and 10×10 ml per group being sufficient for any single experiment. After use they are well rinsed, dried, and sterilized in cans by dry heat. The micro-organisms employed in the experiments are of non-pathogenic groups such as *E.coli*, except for *Salmonella typhimurium* strain LT2. However, this latter strain has been used for many years in laboratory experiments and it is generally agreed to be harmless. Accordingly, the use of unplugged pipettes for dispensing all cultures, including LT2 (saving much time in cleaning and preparing pipettes for re-use) is now common practice, and is considered a safe procedure.

3. *Test-tubes*. Two sizes only are required for most purposes, a $6 \times \frac{5}{8}$ inch ('large') and a $3 \times \frac{1}{2}$ inch ('small'). They are conveniently 'capped' with aluminium slip-on caps and can then be sterilized in racks by dry heat. For some phage preparations a larger ($6 \times \frac{7}{8}$ inch) test-tube is useful. This can be converted into a 'bubbler' by the use of a 5 mm (internal diameter) delivery tube,* plugged at one end and passing through a 1 cm hole bored in the slip-on cap, which is lined with a rubber grommet.†

4. *Bottles*. A wide range of bottles with screw-caps (s/c) with rubber liners in 500 ml (20 oz), 100 ml (4 oz), 25 ml (1 oz) and 10 ml ($\frac{1}{2}$ oz) sizes is very convenient for making up media and growing cultures (see p. 239). The smaller sizes can also be used for centrifuging at low speed. They are sterilized by steam heat.

Other apparatus

1. *Colony or plaque counts*. Many experiments require the counting of

---

* A suitable tube with a constriction for sterility plug is a 9 inch Pasteur pipette (see p. 240).
† Similar bubbler tubes may be made from the small ($3 \times \frac{1}{2}$ inch) test tubes which are useful when small volumes are required to be aerated e.g. see p. 95.

many hundreds of bacterial colonies or plaques. A hand-tally counter is the most economical, but a more sophisticated electronic device (see Appendix K) has obvious advantages.

2. *Ultraviolet source.* A low-pressure, low-emission ultraviolet lamp producing most of its output at 2600 Å is suitable for mutagenic and induction experiments (see pp. 15, 239).

A list of supply houses for many specialized items of equipment is provided in Appendix L.

Experiments 1 to 3
Mutation

Experiment 1
Ultraviolet irradiation survival curve

Background

In a population of bacteria exposed to the lethal action of ultraviolet (u.v.) light, each cell has a certain probability of surviving a given dose of irradiation. If this probability is 0.1, then 10% of the population will survive this dose. Among the survivors, each bacterium has again the same probability of surviving a second similar dose. Thus, if the dose is doubled, the number of survivors will fall according to the product of the probabilities 0.1 × 0.1, *i.e.*, there will be 1% survivors. If a graph is made, plotting the number of survivors against the time of irradiation (or dose), this will give rise to an exponential survival curve. If the logarithm of the number of survivors is plotted against the dose (semi-log plot), the resulting survival curve will be a straight line.

The slope of the survival curve reflects the ease with which the u.v.-sensitive 'target' in the cell can be 'hit' (damaged by a photon). The easier it is to hit the target, the steeper the slope. Some factors which affect the slope are:

1. *Density of the suspension.* Because u.v. penetrates biological tissue poorly, in a dense suspension of bacteria some of the cells are shielded by others, so that the survival curve becomes concave upwards (to a rough approximation, such a curve may appear linear, but of lower slope). In practice, shielding is not an important factor for suspensions containing less than 1×10^8 bacteria per ml.

2. *The nature of the suspending fluid.* Nutrient broth absorbs more u.v. radiation than aqueous buffer solutions, so that the effective dose for bacteria suspended in broth is reduced. Also, toxic, organic peroxides may be produced in irradiated broth which will prolong the effect of the irradiation beyond the actual time of exposure to the u.v. source.

3. *The physiological condition of the cells.* In a large cell the u.v.-sensitive target, which is essentially the deoxyribonucleic acid (DNA) of the bacterial nucleus, is usually smaller relative to the cell volume than in a small cell.

The shape of a survival curve depends upon the number of 'hits' necessary to kill the cell and the number of u.v.-sensitive targets within it. A multi-nucleate cell can survive u.v. radiation provided that one nucleus remains undamaged. At low doses, the u.v.-radiation survival curve for a population of such multi-nucleate cells will therefore have a plateau or 'shoulder', because the probability that *each* nucleus in the multinucleate cell receives a lethal hit will be low, and most of the cells will survive. At higher doses, the majority of cells will receive a lethal number of hits and the survival curve will then become exponential.

The most lethal and mutagenic wavelength for u.v. radiation is 2600 Å which is the u.v. absorption peak for DNA. *In vitro* studies have shown that purines are relatively resistant to chemical alteration by u.v. light, but pyrimidines are altered in at least two ways. One of these, called 'hydration', involves addition of water across the 5,6-double bond. This reaction has not been proven to be of biological significance. The other involves the formation of *pyrimidine dimers*, chiefly of the thymine-thymine type, which are biologically important (WACKER, 1963). For example thymine-dimers have been shown to be responsible for a large part of the photoreactivable portion of the u.v. damage to transforming DNA (SETLOW & SETLOW, 1963).

Two mechanisms for the repair of u.v. damage to bacteria can be distinguished. One, 'dark repair', is carried out by an enzyme in the absence of visible light. The other, 'light repair', is carried out by enzyme action only in the presence of visible light. Mutants have been isolated which are unable to carry out 'dark repair' and these have, as a consequence, very much steeper u.v.-survival curves (RÖRSCH *et al.* 1963; HARM, 1963; SAUERBIER, 1962; HOWARD-FLANDERS *et al.*, 1962).

Since bacteria possess mechanisms for repairing u.v. damage both in the light and in the dark, post-irradiation incubation conditions will influence survival. It is therefore very important to use standardized conditions and procedures to obtain reproducible results.

Some prophages can be induced by low doses of u.v. radiation. In the case of bacteria lysogenized by such prophages, fewer cells will survive than in a 'cured' or non-lysogenic strain.

References

HARM W. (1963) *Z. Vererbungslehre*, **94**, 67.

HOWARD-FLANDERS P., R.P.BOYCE & L.THERIOT (1962) *Nature*, **195**, 51.

RÖRSCH A., A.EDELMAN & T.A.COHEN (1963) *Biochim. Biophys. Acta.* **68**, 263.

SAUERBIER W. (1962) *Z. Vererbungslehre*, **93**, 220.

SETLOW J.K. & R.B.SETLOW (1963) *Nature*, **197**, 560.

WACKER A. (1963) In: *Progress in Nucleic Acid Research*, Eds. J.N. Davidson and W.Cohen, vol. 1, pp.369–399. Academic Press: London and New York.
WITKIN E.M. (1947) *Genetics* 32, 221.

Intention

The purpose of this experiment is two-fold:
1. to demonstrate and measure the sensitivity of *Escherichia coli* K12 to ultraviolet radiation,
2. to provide experience in dilution and plating techniques.

Requirements

Part 1   50 ml of an o/n broth culture of *Escherichia coli* K12, non-lysogenic for phage λ (EMG10 or 14. See Appendix B)

24 nutrient agar (NA) plates.

300 ml buffer

6 glass petri dishes, selected with flat bottoms (see below).

19 large tubes.

1 × 100 ml bottle.

2 × 25 ml bottles.

u.v. lamp. A 15 watt low-pressure Hanovia 'Bactericidal' lamp is suitable. But any lamp which gives a uniform beam of u.v. having about 90% of the emission at 2600 Å will suffice. The output of a new lamp may be calibrated in $erg/mm^2/sec$ using a u.v. intensity meter, or it can be calibrated biologically by measuring the u.v.-inactivation of bacteriophage T2 or *E.coli*.

[60 erg/mm^2 inactivates approx. 90% of T2 particles. 100 erg/mm^2 inactivates approx. 99% of T2 particles. 500 erg/mm^2 inactivates approx. 99% of a λ-lysogenic strain of *E.coli* K12, e.g. EMG2.]

Method

1 Switch on the u.v. lamp one hour before use to stabilize the emission, and set it at a distance of 50 cm above the work bench.

2 Prepare 10 × 10 ml dilution tubes
         9 × 9 ml dilution tubes.

3 Centrifuge the o/n broth culture (2 samples of 25 ml) and resuspend each pellet in 25 ml buffer. Pool the two suspensions in 100 ml bottle. Adjust to a total cell population density of approx. 1×10^8 bacteria per ml.

4 Irradiate aliquots of 7 ml of the suspension in flat-bottomed, glass petri dishes for the times indicated, agitating the suspension gently. Accurate timing is achieved by removing the lid for the required period. Note that plastic dishes are unsuitable, having an unwettable surface on which small volumes of fluid will not flow out uniformly.

5 Dilute as indicated and spread 0.1 ml of each dilution on each of two NA plates.

u.v. dose (erg/mm²/sec)	0	100	200	300	400	500
*Time (sec)	0	20	40	60	80	100
Dilutions:	10^{-6}	10^{-5}	10^{-5}	10^{-5}	10^{-4}	10^{-4}
	10^{-5}	10^{-4}	10^{-4}	10^{-4}	10^{-3}	10^{-3}

* Exposure time in seconds for a Hanovia bactericidal u.v. lamp at 50 cm distance.

6 Incubate plates overnight.

Day following Part 1

1 Count the colonies.

2 Calculate the number of surviving bacteria per ml at each u.v. dose.

3 Plot the logarithm of the surviving fraction against the u.v. dose.

Experiment 2
The induction, isolation and analysis of auxotrophic mutants

Background

From large populations of bacteria, rare mutant cells which can survive and grow on a medium which restricts the growth of the 'wild-type' parent strain can readily be isolated. For example, colonies derived from cells which have mutated to drug resistance can be selected by plating large populations of sensitive bacteria on media containing the drug. Similarly, nutritional independence of a growth factor required by the parental strain can be selected by plating large populations of cells on media lacking the growth factor.

Nutritionally-deficient (auxotrophic) mutants obviously cannot be isolated in this way. A method facilitating the isolation of these mutants, developed by DAVIS (1948), is based on the fact that penicillin kills only growing bacteria. Cells of the nutritionally non-exacting (prototrophic) wild-type strain of *E.coli* K12 will grow in a medium containing only inorganic salts and glucose (minimal medium), and are killed if penicillin is present. Nutritionally-deficient mutants which cannot grow in this medium will survive this penicillin treatment. The addition of penicillin to growing cultures of cells therefore increases the proportion among the survivors of any auxotrophic mutants that may be present.

Auxotrophic mutants in *E.coli* K12 are usually present in very low numbers (about 1 in 10⁴) but this proportion can be considerably increased by treating a culture with a mutagen (mutagenesis).

The mutagen of choice is N-methyl-N'-nitro-N-nitrosoguanidine (NTG). Under certain conditions over 40% of the survivors of NTG treatment may be auxotrophic (ADELBERG, MANDEL & CHEN, 1965). After mutagenesis, the treated cells are sub-cultured in broth to allow the segregation of mutant and non-mutant nuclei from multi-nucleate cells and to permit the phenotypic expression of the induced mutations (WITKIN, 1956). The culture is then washed free of broth and a suitable inoculum seeded into minimal medium containing penicillin. After penicillin treatment, the survivors are plated on nutrient agar on which both wild-type and auxotrophs can form colonies. The auxotrophic mutants are identified by their failure to grow after replica-plating to minimal medium. The specific growth-factor requirements of the mutants isolated in this way are identified by streaking them on minimal agar supplemented with various combinations of amino acids, vitamins, purines and pyrimidines (HOLLIDAY, 1956).

References

ADELBERG E.A., M.MANDEL & G.C.C.CHEN (1965) *Biochem. Biophys. Res. Comm.* **18**, 788.

DAVIS B.D. (1948) *J. Amer. Chem. Soc.* **70**, 4267.

HOLLIDAY R. (1956) *Nature* **178**, 987.

LEDERBERG J. (1950) In: *Methods in Medical Research* (ed. J.H.Comrie, Jr.) **3**, 5. Year Book Publishers: Chicago.

WITKIN E.M. (1956) *Cold Spr. Harb. Symp. Quant. Biol.* **21**, 123.

Intention

This experiment is designed to demonstrate:
  (i) the potency of a mutagenic agent, nitrosoguanidine (NTG),
 (ii) penicillin selection and,
(iii) isolation and characterization of auxotrophic mutants.

Requirements

Part 1   5 ml log. broth culture of wild-type *E.coli* K12 (EMG2)

2 × 5 ml broth.

1 ml freshly prepared, aqueous solution of N-methyl-N′ nitro-N-nitrosoguanidine (NTG) (3 mg/ml).

20 ml buffer.

Part 2   10 ml liquid minimal medium (MM) plus penicillin (200 units per ml, freshly prepared in 1 oz s/c bottle).

18 nutrient agar (NA) plates.

50 ml buffer.

3 large tubes.

Part 3   6 minimal agar (MA) plates.

Replicating block and sterile velveteens.

Part 4   4 NA plates.
          4 MA plates.
          100 ml buffer.
          Small tubes (up to 100).
          Template (Appendix F).

Part 5   12 MA plates supplemented with amino-acid pools, vitamin pool, purine and pyrimidine pool (see Appendix E).

Part 6   MA plates supplemented with individual amino acids, vitamins, purines and pyrimidines (as required).

Part 7   NA slopes (as required).

Method

Part 1   **1** Centrifuge the 5 ml broth culture of wild-type
1 hr   *E.coli* K12 and resuspend the pellet in 5 ml of fresh broth in a ½ oz s/c bottle.

          2 Add 0.05 ml of solution of NTG to give a final concentration of 30 μg/ml.* (Handle NTG with caution; it is an extremely potent mutagen and a skin irritant.)

          3 Incubate the NTG-treated cells for 15 min at 37° in a water-bath.

          4 Centrifuge and wash twice in buffer to remove NTG.†

          5 Transfer 0.1 ml of the washed cell suspension to 5 ml broth in a ½ oz bottle and incubate overnight.

---

* Higher concentrations of NTG yield more mutants, but many of them have complex nutritional requirements due to multiple mutation.
† Alternatively, the NTG can be rapidly removed by filtration through a membrane, followed by rinsing and resuspension of the bacteria (see p.44).

Day following Part 1

Part 2
15 min followed by ½ hr–6 hr later

1 Prepare 3×9 ml dilution tubes.

2 Dilute the mutagenized culture 10^{-1} in buffer and transfer 0.1 ml to 10 ml of liquid MM plus penicillin. Incubate for 6 hr at 37° with aeration on a rotor (33 rpm turntable).

3 Dilute 10^{-1} and 10^{-2} in buffer. Spread 0.1 ml of the undiluted culture, and the 10^{-1} and 10^{-2} dilutions, on each of six NA plates, i.e. a total of 18 plates.

4 Incubate the plates overnight. (Store the penicillin-treated cell suspension overnight in a refrigerator. It can be used again next day if there are too many, or too few, colonies on the NA plates.)

Day following Part 2

Part 3
15 min

1 Select the best 6 plates having about 20–100 well-isolated colonies per plate.

2 Replicate each plate onto MA, remembering to mark reference points on all plates.

3 Incubate the plates overnight.

Day following Part 3

Part 4
1–2 hr

1 Prepare 100×1 ml tubes of buffer.

2 Examine and compare the master and replica plates by lining up the reference marks, superimposing the replica above the master plate. Mark, on the back of the master plate, those colonies which do NOT grow on the MA plates. These are presumptive mutants.

3 Pick them by touching each colony with a sterile loop and suspend each one in 1 ml of buffer in a small tube. Number the suspensions of each presumptive mutant carefully. (About 60 such operations can be performed in an hour.)

4 Streak each suspension on NA and MA plates to test whether they are mutants or replication failures. About 25 small streaks can be accommodated on one plate using a marked template (see Appendix F).

5 Incubate plates overnight. Keep the suspensions in a refrigerator overnight.

Day following Part 4

Part 5
1 hr

1 Examine the plates and discard any suspensions which gave growth on BOTH NA and MA plates.

2 Using the same marked template, streak the suspensions of the remaining mutants which grew only on NA on the series of MA plates supplemented with amino-acid pools, the vitamin pool, and the purine and pyrimidine pool (Appendix E).

3 Incubate the plates overnight.

Day following Part 5

Part 6
1 hr

1 Examine the plates and identify the specific nutritional requirement of each mutant (see Appendix E).

2 Confirm the nutritional requirement of each mutant by streaking it from the suspension onto MA supplemented with the appropriate growth factor.

3 Incubate the plates overnight.

Day following Part 6

Part 7
$\frac{1}{2}$ hr

Examine the plates and confirm the identity of the specific requirement of each mutant. Select the mutants required and maintain them on NA slopes or as stab cultures.

Experiment 3
The Luria and Delbrück fluctuation test

Background

When virulent bacteriophage is added to a turbid culture of bacterial cells which are sensitive to the phage, after a few hours the culture becomes clear due to multiplication of the virus inside the cells which ultimately burst (or lyse) to release the particles of phage progeny. After further incubation, the culture may again become turbid due to the growth of bacteria which are resistant to the bacteriophage.

Two hypotheses have been advanced to account for the origin of these resistant variants:

1. *The adaptation hypothesis*, according to which every cell has a small probability of being induced by the phage to adapt itself so that it can survive and grow in the presence of the phage, this adaptation then being passed on to its descendants.

2. *The spontaneous-mutation hypothesis*, which states that every cell has a small probability of mutating during its life-time from phage-sensitivity to phage-resistance, whether phage is present or not. The progeny of such a resistant cell will also be resistant unless back-mutation occurs.

LURIA & DELBRÜCK (1943) devised the *fluctuation test* to decide between these two hypotheses. An important difference between the two alternative ideas is that, according to the adaptation hypothesis, the bacterial population is homogeneous before the phage is added. Whilst, according to the mutation hypothesis, the population is not homogeneous, since mutation to resistance may occur at any time during the growth of the culture before the phage is added. The number of bacteria resistant to the phage will thus depend upon whether the first mutation to phage-resistance occurred early or late in the growth of the culture.

Thus, according to the adaptation hypothesis the probability of any bacterium becoming resistant after contact with the phage should be the same for all the bacteria in the culture. The adaptation hypothesis therefore predicts that there will be no large fluctuations in the numbers of resistant bacteria from culture to culture in a parallel series to which phage is added. The fluctuations should in fact be no greater than those encountered in a series of samples all taken from the same culture.

On the other hand, according to the hypothesis of spontaneous muta-tion, the time of occurrence of a mutation in a series of parallel cultures will be subject to random variation. Cultures in which a mutation occurs early will contain large clones (large numbers) of resistant cells, while cultures in which mutation occurs late will contain small clones (very few) resis-tant cells. In other words, the mutation hypothesis predicts that resistant bacteria will arise as clones in the culture, whilst the adaptation hypothesis does not. The mutation hypothesis thus leads to the prediction that there will be larger fluctuations in the numbers of resistant mutants from culture to culture in a parallel series, than from a series of samples taken from the same culture.

The experimental test therefore consists in determining the numbers of resistant bacteria present in two series of samples, one series from parallel cultures and the other series taken from the same bulk culture. The experiment carried out by Luria and Delbrück measured resistance to phage T1 in *E.coli B*, and the variance calculated from the number of resistant bacteria in a series of ten samples from the same culture was found to be 54, while the variance for the samples taken from 10 parallel cultures was 3498. Clearly, the variance between parallel and independent cultures was greater than the variance between samples taken from the same culture, indicating that the spontaneous-mutation hypothesis is correct.

The fluctuation test has been applied to investigate the origin of a large number of different types of bacterial variant in several bacterial species. The characters investigated include resistance to bacteriophages of various kinds, resistance to various antibiotic drugs (e.g. streptomycin, penicillin, sulphonamide) and to radiation, independence of growth-factor require-ments, and the ability to ferment various carbohydrates. In each case the variants have shown a 'clonal' distribution indicative of mutation.

References
LURIA, S.E. & M.DELBRÜCK (1943) *Genetics*, **28**, 491.

Intention

The experiment is designed:
1 to apply the fluctuation test to determine the origin of resistant variants to phage T6 in *E.coli K12* and,
2 to measure the mutation rate from T6-sensitivity to T6-resistance.

N.B. Some cultures of *E.coli* contain variants which produce large, mucoid colonies due to the production of polysaccharide material. These bacteria are genetically sensitive to phage T6 but they are able to form colonies in the presence of T6 because the polysaccharide prevents the phage from adsorbing to the cell wall. Thus, only those colonies which have the normal (i.e. non-mucoid) *E.coli* morphology should be scored when counting the numbers of T6-resistant clones.

Requirements

Part 1   1 ml of an o/n broth culture of *E.coli* K12 (EMG1) sensitive to phage T6 (*T6-s*).
100 ml broth.
100 ml buffer.
4 large tubes.
10 small tubes.

Part 2   5.0 ml of phage T6 at a concentration of at least 5×10^{10} particles/ml.
24 NA plates.
100 ml buffer.
6 large tubes.

Method

Part 1
½ hr

1 Prepare 1 large tube of 10 ml broth
      10 small tubes of 1 ml broth
      3 dilution tubes (2×10 ml; 1×9 ml).

2 Dilute the bacterial culture 10^{-5}.

3 Add 0.1 ml of this dilution to each of the 10 small, broth tubes. (These tubes comprise the parallel series of cultures.)

4 Add 1 ml of this dilution to the 10 ml of broth in a large tube. (This tube is the large volume culture.)

5 Incubate all the tubes overnight.

Day following Part 1

Part 2
½ hr

1 Prepare 6×10 ml dilution tubes.

2 Spread 0.2 ml of the T6 phage suspension on each of 20 NA plates. Spread the suspension evenly over the whole surface taking special care to ensure that it is spread out to the edges of the plate. Allow a few minutes for the plates to dry.

3 Spread 0.1 ml from each of the 10 small tubes in the parallel series, each on a separate plate seeded with the phage. Spread the bacteria evenly over the surface taking special care to *avoid* spreading it to the outer edges of the plate.

4 Similarly spread 0.1 ml aliquots from the large tube onto each of the remaining 10 plates previously seeded with phage T6.

5 Pool the small cultures. Assay the number of viable bacteria by diluting 10^{-6} and spreading 0.1 ml onto each of two NA plates. Similarly assay the large culture.

6 Incubate all the plates overnight.

Day following Part 2.

1 Count the number of T6-resistant colonies on each of the phage-spread plates. Calculate the variance for each series of samples separately.

$$\text{Variance} = \frac{\sum (x - \bar{x})^2}{n - 1}$$

$\bar{x} =$ mean of the observed numbers of T6-resistant colonies.

$x =$ observed number of T6-resistant colonies in each sample.

$n =$ number of observations, *i.e.* 10.

2 Compare the two values obtained. Is the origin of phage T6-resistant variants best explained by the adaptation hypothesis or by the mutation hypothesis?

3 Count the number of colonies on the four assay plates (total viable bacteria). Calculate the number of bacteria per sample taken from the two sets of cultures. Calculate the mutation rate $T6\text{-}s \rightarrow T6\text{-}r$ from the formula:

$$r = aNt \log (aNtC) \quad \text{(Luria and Delbrück, 1943)}$$

$r =$ average number of mutants per sample.

$C =$ number of cultures or samples, *i.e.* 10.

$a =$ mutation rate.

$Nt =$ number of bacteria per sample.

Example: $r = 30$
$C = 10$
$Nt = 2 \times 10^8$

From the graph of r plotted against aNt for various values of C (see Appendix G), we see that when $r = 30$, $aNt = 7.5$.

Therefore, $30 = a \times 2 \times 10^8 \log 75$

Therefore, $a = \dfrac{30}{2 \times 10^8 \times 1.875} = 8 \times 10^{-8}$

Experiments 4, 5 and 6
The biochemical characterization of mutants

Background

From the work of BEADLE and TATUM in 1941, it was clear that genes exert their function through enzymes, and that an alteration in the structure of a gene by mutation leads to an alteration in the structure of the corresponding enzyme, usually resulting in loss of its function. By the isolation and analysis of many such 'biochemical' mutants, it was found that most of the simple monomers or building blocks such as amino acids, purines, and pyrimidines, which are polymerized to form the macromolecules of the cell, are synthesized by a series of small steps, each step under the control of an enzyme and forming a biochemical or metabolic pathway. Thus, the biosynthesis of such a compound Z would be carried out by means of the pathway shown in Fig.2, in which the three enzymes, a, b, c, controlled respectively by the genes α, β, and γ, act successively to transform a precursor W, through the intermediates X and Y, to the end product Z.

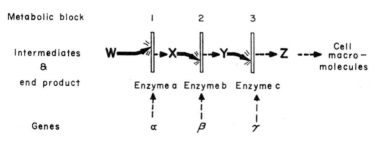

Fig.2 Biochemical blocks in a metabolic pathway

When a series of biochemical mutants have been isolated and characterized with regard to their end-product requirement (amino acid, purine, pyrimidine, or vitamin, etc, see p. 17), the more precise identification of the metabolic block can then be investigated. Thus, if a series of genetically non-identical mutants, all of which require the same end product are available, determination of the exact nutritional requirements and the results of cross-feeding and accumulation of intermediates by these mutants can be used to construct the metabolic pathway which is used by the cell for the synthesis of this particular end product.

A group of mutants which respond to a particular end requirement is first sub-divided on the basis of the two complementary tests of cross-feeding and the accumulation of intermediates. Both tests are based on the assumption that a single mutation will affect only one step in a particular metabolic sequence, e.g. in the hypothetical pathway shown above, a single mutation will block the conversion of either W to X, or X to Y, or Y to Z, but usually not more than one of these conversions.* For example, a mutation in gene α will usually manifest itself in the absence of a enzyme activity, leading to a biochemical block between W and X. Since W is not metabolized to X, it is therefore usually accumulated by cells blocked in this position on the metabolic pathway, and may be identified in the culture filtrates of mutants of gene α.

A further technique investigates the cross-feeding (syntrophism) of mutants having the same end requirement, and relies on the accumulation and diffusion of these intermediate compounds. Thus, if the compound accumulated and diffusing from one mutant is one which comes after the block of a second mutant, the cells of the latter will be able to utilize it for growth. Accordingly, a mutant which is blocked at the terminal step should be able to support the growth of mutants blocked at any one of the preceding steps. By cross-feeding experiments, mutants can therefore be arranged in the sequential order of steps of the metabolic pathway; but this method does not give any information about the chemical nature of the intermediates.

However, if a compound identified as an intermediate is supplied from without (exogenously), it should be able to support growth of mutants in which the block occurs at an earlier stage in the metabolic pathway, e.g. a mutant blocked at position 1 should be able to grow if supplied with either X or Y as an alternative to Z. Similarly, mutants blocked at position 2 should grow if supplied with Y or Z. However, when interpreting this kind of test it should be borne in mind that cells are not freely permeable to all compounds.

---

* Exceptions to this occur in a number of cases. For example, a block in the synthesis of an intermediate which is common to more than one pathway will simultaneously impose multiple requirements. Also some 'deletions' of the genetic material may be extensive enough to alter two or more contiguous genes and so affect more than one step in a biochemical pathway or more than one pathway.

References

AMES B.N. (1955) In: *A Symposium on Amino-Acid Metabolism*, p. 357. McElroy and Glass, eds. Johns Hopkins Press: Baltimore.

AMES B.N. & P.E.HARTMAN (1962) In: *The Molecular Basis of Neoplasia*, p.322. The University of Texas Press: Austin.

BEADLE G.W. & E.L.TATUM (1941) *Proc. Nat. Acad. Sci., Wash.*, **27**, 499.

BRENNER S. (1955) *Proc. Nat. Acad. Sci., Wash.*, **41**, 862.

DAVIS B.D. (1950) *Experientia*, **6**, 41.

DAVIS B.D. & E.S.MINGIOLI (1950) *J. Bact.* **60**, 17.

HAYES W. (1968) *The Genetics of Bacteria and their Viruses*, p.87 *et seq.* Blackwell: Oxford.

TATUM E.L., *et al.* (1954) *Proc. Nat. Acad. Sci., Wash.*, **40**, 271.

UMBARGER E. & B.D.DAVIS (1962) In: *The Bacteria*, Vol. III, I.C.Gunsalus and R.Y.Stanier, eds. Academic Press: London and New York.

Experiment 4
Cross-feeding tests

Intention

This experiment investigates the cross-feeding between four tryptophan-requiring mutants of *Salmonella typhimurium*, strain LT2, which have different metabolic blocks in the pathway of tryptophan biosynthesis. The mutants *trpA8*- (EMG39), *trpB4*- (EMG41), *trpC3*- (EMG42), and *trpD1*- (EMG43) should be streaked and incubated overnight on NA plates to produce single colonies.

Requirements

Part 1   *Class*
          o/n cultures of the four *S.typhimurium* strains *trpA*-, *trpB*-, *trpC*-, and *trpD*- on nutrient agar (NA) plates (stock plates).

          Group
          4 minimal agar (MA) plates.
          5 ml buffer.
          4 small tubes.

Method

Part 1
15 min

1 Prepare 4 small tubes containing 1 ml buffer.

2 With a sterile loop remove some of the bacterial growth from one of the plates and make a suspension (*c.*10^9 organisms/ml) in 1 ml of buffer. Repeat for each of the other three tryptophan-requiring auxotrophs.

3 With a loopful of the first suspension make a two-inch long streak across a minimal agar plate. Make equivalent streaks from each of the other three mutant suspensions perpendicular to the first streak, but separated from it at one end by about 3 mm (see Fig.3).

4 Prepare similar plates using each of the other three mutants in turn for the initial streak.

5 Label the plates carefully and incubate for 48 hr.

Two days following Part 1

Part 2
15 min

1 Note the areas of growth on each of the plates. Mutants will cross-feed, or show syntrophy, when they lie sufficiently close to one another to permit adequate diffusion of excreted metabolites.

2 From your results, assess the order of the metabolic blocks.

Conclusions

The diagram below (Fig.3) shows the appearance of a typical plate streaked with four auxotrophs. The areas of growth indicate that *B* feeds *A*, *C*, and *D* and that *D* feeds *A* and *C*. Thus the biochemical blocks in mutants *A* and *C* precede that of *D*, which precedes that of *B* in the pathway. We would conclude from such a test that the order of the pathway was

$$(A,C) \to D \to B$$

The relative order of *A* and *C* can be distinguished from the other plates.

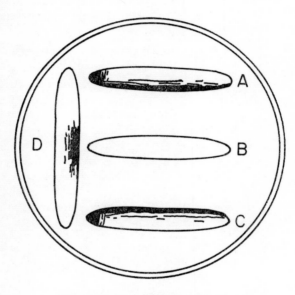

Fig.3 Streaking for syntrophism

Experiment 5
Accumulation studies

Intention

The cross-feeding experiments give no clue as to the chemical identity of the intermediates involved. This information may be obtained by making use of the fact that when mutants are grown in the presence of sub-optimal (limiting) amounts* of the end requirement, many will accumulate, to different levels, the intermediates involved before the block. These accumulated intermediates can then be isolated from culture filtrates of the mutants, and after purification, may be identified and checked by their ability to support growth of other mutants. This experiment sets out to identify a series of intermediates which are accumulated by a number of biochemically-related tryptophan-requiring mutants of *E.coli*.

Requirements

Part 1   4 NA plates each streaked for single colonies of one of the tryptophan auxotrophs of *E.coli* K12 (EMG 3,4,5 and 6) (stock plates).
50 ml liquid MM supplemented with 5μg L-tryptophan/ml (sub-optimal concentration).
10 ml buffer.
4 small tubes.
4 large tubes.

Part 2   0.5 ml anthranilic acid (2 mg/ml in buffer).
0.5 ml indole   (2 mg/ml in buffer).
0.5 ml L-tryptophan   (2 mg/ml in buffer).
1 ml Ehrlich's reagent (10% para-dimethyl-amino-benzaldehyde in conc. HCl. Immediately before use, dilute with 4 vol of acetone. This is a general reagent which produces a purple colour with indoles.

---

* To be determined by experiment. A concentration is used which will support *c*.50% of maximal growth of the particular mutant.

33

Method

Part 1
15 min

1 Prepare 4 tubes each containing 10 ml MM + tryptophan at 5 μg/ml.
Prepare 4 small tubes of 1 ml buffer.

2 Take an inoculum from each of the four plates of the tryptophan auxotrophs each into 1 ml buffer to produce a suspension of cells of about 10^8/ml. Take 0.1 ml from each suspension into 10 ml minimal medium containing a limiting amount (5 μg/ml) of L-tryptophan and incubate for 7 days.

One week following Part 1

Part 2
$\frac{1}{2}$ hr

1 After growth, separate the cells from the supernatants by centrifugation at low speed (10 min at 3000 g).

2 Apply single drops of each supernatant and of the three reference solutions, anthranilic acid, indole and L-tryptophan to a filter-paper disc (mark the positions).

3 When the spots have dried, examine them under ultraviolet light. (Beware of harmful exposure to your eyes.) Anthranilic acid yields a characteristic blue-violet fluorescence, whereas indole and tryptophan show dark spots due to absorption of u.v., thus preventing the natural fluorescence of the paper.

4 Then add 1 drop of Ehrlich's reagent to each spot and re-examine in ordinary light. Tryptophan, indole and indole glycerophosphate, being indoles, give a purple colour, contrasting with the yellow colour of anthranilic acid.
Compare the reactions of the known and unknown substances and note carefully which are accumulated by which strains.

This type of test is of very limited value and must be supplemented by other analytical tests of the accumulated substances, e.g. chromatographic analysis, determination of absorption spectra, etc. Accumulation studies can be misleading in cases where an intermediate is unstable, e.g. the spontaneous conversion of prephenic acid to phenylpyruvic acid under acid conditions, (see HAYES, 1968, p.120).

Experiment 6
Growth on purified intermediates

Intention

In the study of an unknown metabolic pathway, information of the kind obtained in the previous experiment is the most rudimentary necessary for the chemical identification of a certain compound as an intermediate in a particular biochemical pathway. If little is known of the intermediates involved, the first essential step is to obtain sufficient of each intermediate, by accumulation studies, in a highly purified form so as to permit analyses for chemical elements, the determination of molecular weight, absorption spectra and the preparation of derivative compounds. Using this knowledge, the chemical identity of the intermediate can be suggested and then checked using synthetic or carefully purified biochemicals to support growth of the auxotrophs.

This experiment is designed to show the specific growth responses of the four *S.typhimurium* auxotrophs to known intermediates.

Requirements

Class

Part 1   4 o/n NA plates of *S.typhimurium* auxotrophs (EMG 39, 41, 42 and 43) requiring tryptophan (stock plates).

Group

4 MA plates, labelled A to D, supplemented with
  (A) 20 μg/ml anthranilic acid
  (B) 20 μg/ml indole
  (C) 20 μg/ml tryptophan
  (D) Unsupplemented.
5 ml buffer.
4 small tubes.

36

Method

Part 1
15 min

1 Prepare 4 × 1 ml buffer tubes.

2 Take an inoculum with a wire loop from each plate culture and make a separate suspension (*c.*10[8] organisms/ml) in 1 ml buffer.

3 With a sterile loop make a well-separated streak (to avoid syntrophism) from each suspension on each MA plate, A to D, labelling carefully on the under-surface of the plate.

4 Incubate overnight. (Prolonged incubation may lead to the appearance of revertant colonies, possibly leading to a false positive result.)

Day following Part 1

Part 2
½ hr

Notice the growth response of each mutant on each of the four supplemented plates. Correlate the results of this experiment with those on the nature of the accumulants and the cross-feeding tests; prepare a full biochemical characterization of the mutants supplied and construct a biochemical pathway.

Note to Instructors

Interest can be added to this series of experiments by labelling the strains in a known arbitrary manner before issuing them to students.

Experiments 7 to 10
Synthesis and properties of DNA: Transformation

Experiment 7
The isolation of thymine-requiring mutants

Background

The isolation of mutants unable to synthesize thymine was rarely reported until a selective system for their isolation was developed. For reasons that are still only partially known, *E.coli* mutants which require thymine can grow in the presence of aminopterin and thymine much better than thymine-independent strains, despite the ample supply of thymine. Thus, by prolonged incubation in a medium containing aminopterin, any thymine auxotrophs that arise by mutation will outgrow other cells and can then be isolated by the technique of replica-plating. Thymineless mutants of other species of bacteria can also be isolated by this method with suitable variations in aminopterin concentrations. Since aminopterin penetrates bacterial cells only with difficulty, high concentrations are required to produce mutants in this way.

References
OKADA T., K.YANAGISAWA & F.J.RYAN (1961) *Z. Verebungslehre*, **92**, 403.
STACEY K.A. & E.SIMSON (1965) *J. Bacteriol.*, **90**, 554.

Intention

This experiment is designed to afford experience in the isolation of thymineless mutants of *E.coli*. The mutants isolated by this technique need high concentrations of thymine (*c*.50 µg/ml) whether grown on plates or in liquid media. A further mutation can occur which allows growth in concentrations below 5 µg/ml.

Requirements

Part 1
: 0.5 ml of o/n culture of *E.coli* K12, methionine-requiring mutant 58–161 (EMG1), grown in M9 + methionine medium.

  25 ml of M9 medium (Appendix A13) containing 20 μg/ml methionine (M9 + met).

  2.5 ml of aminopterin (3.5 mg/ml) dissolved in 0.01N NaOH.

  1.0 ml of 0.1N HCl.

  2.0 ml of thymine (0.5 mg/ml).

  5 ml of buffer.

  4 large tubes.

Part 3
: 4 nutrient agar (NA) plates containing 50 μg/ml thymine (NA + thy).

  50 ml buffer.

  3 large tubes.

Part 4
: 2 minimal agar (MA) plates containing 20 μg/ml methionine (MA + met).

  2 MA plates containing 20 μg/ml methionine + 50 μg/ml thymine (MA + met + thy).

  Replica plating block and velvets.

Part 5
: 3 NA + thy plates.

Method

Part 1
½ hr

1 Set up and inoculate 4 large tubes A, B, C and D as under:

	A	B	C	D
M9 + met	5 ml	5 ml	5 ml	5 ml
aminopterin	—	—	1 ml	1 ml
0.1N HCl (to neutralize NaOH in which aminopterin is dissolved)	—	—	0.1 ml	0.1 ml
buffer	1 ml	1 ml	—	—
thymine (0.5 mg/ml)	0.5 ml	0.5 ml	—	0.5 ml
bacterial culture	—	0.1 ml	0.1 ml	0.1 ml

Tube A—test of sterility of medium.
Tube B—test of normal growth of bacteria.
Tube C—test of effect of aminopterin.
Tube D—test of effect of thymine.

2 Incubate tubes overnight.

Day following Part 1

Part 2
15 min

1 Examine tubes after 24 hr. If there is growth in A or no growth in B, discard the experiment.

2 Record the turbidity in C and D and continue incubation for a further 24 hr.

Day following Part 2

Part 3
15 min

1 Prepare 3 dilution tubes (2 × 10 ml; 1 × 9 ml).

2 If there is good growth in D and little in C, dilute an aliquot of D to 10^{-4} and 10^{-5} and spread 0.1 ml on each of 2 (NA + thy) plates from both dilutions.

3 Incubate the plates overnight.

Day following Part 3

Part 4   **1** Select the pair of plates which show about 100
15 min   well-isolated colonies.

2 Replicate each plate to MA + met and MA +
met + thy.

3 Incubate plates for 48 hr.

Two days following Part 4

Part 5   **1** Compare the growth of each colony on the two
15 min   media. Approximately 50% of the colonies should
be *thy⁻* and grow only on MA + met + thy. (This
number may be as low as 1% with other strains.)
Select three *thy⁻* colonies.

2 Purify each colony by restreaking for single colonies
on NA + thy.

Experiment 8
Thymineless death

Background

Cells unable to synthesize protein or RNA survive many hours without loss of the ability to form colonies, even if this restriction is imposed by starving the cells of an amino acid or of a purine which they are unable to synthesize. There seems to be only a few minor exceptions to this rule. For instance, cells prevented from making cell walls while still able to carry out all other syntheses become osmotically unstable, but they can be protected from lysis by culture in a medium of high osmotic strength and often recover their ability to form colonies when the inhibition is removed. However, an interference with DNA synthesis by depriving the cells of their supply of thymine has a quite different effect: after a lag of 30 to 40 minutes, thymine-starved cells lose their capacity to form colonies. This loss occurs exponentially, with a half-life between 5 and 15 minutes at 37°. The effect can be easily observed in strains unable to synthesize thymine, but it can also be seen in cells in which thymine synthesis is sufficiently blocked by metabolic inhibitors such as sulphanilamide, aminopterin or fluorodeoxyruridine. The causes of this effect are still obscure. Only one fact is well established; if the rate of RNA synthesis is severely restricted, then the rate of loss of viability is also greatly reduced.

Thymine starvation also causes the induction of phage development in cells lysogenic for a u.v.-inducible prophage.

References
BARNER H.D. & S.S.COHEN (1954) *Proc. Nat. Acad. Sci., Wash.*, **40**, 885.
BARNER H.D. & S.S.COHEN (1955) *J. Bact.* **71**, 588.
MELECHEN N.D. (1964) *Virology*, **23**, 333.

Intention

This experiment is designed to show the rapid loss of viability of a thymine-requiring strain of *E.coli B* (B3) when starved of thymine.

Requirements

Part 1   1 ml of an o/n culture of a *thy⁻* mutant of *E.coli B*
(EMG34) grown in M9 + 2 μg/ml thymine.

16 nutrient agar (NA) plates enriched with 5 μg/ml
thymine (NA + thy).

10 ml M9 medium (Appendix A13) containing
2 μg/ml thymine.

25 ml M9 medium.

150 ml buffer.

1 bacterial membrane filter (Millipore: grade RA;
Oxoid: standard grade).

13 large tubes.

2 large aeration (bubbler) tubes.

Method

Part 1*a*
3½ hr

1 Prepare 13 dilution tubes (7 × 10 ml; 6 × 9 ml).

2 Add 10 ml M9 + 2 μg/ml thymine to one bubbler tube. Label tube *A*. Place in 37° bath.

3 Add 10 ml M9 to other bubbler tube. Label tube *B*. Place in 37° bath.

4 Place remainder of M9 medium in 37° bath.

5 Dilute 0.5 ml of the overnight culture of *E.coli* strain provided into tube *A*.

6 Aerate by bubbling until the bacterial titre is *c*.1 × 10^8 (total count) (about 3 hr).

Part 1*b*
3 hr

Note: All the following operations should be carried out in the 37° room if possible.

1 Filter the culture in tube *A*, rinse the bacteria on the membrane filter by running through 10 ml warm M9; resuspend the bacteria by shaking the filter in half the original volume (5 ml) of warm M9.

2 Dilute 0.1 ml from tube *A* into tube *B* (time 0).

3 Aerate tube *B* gently at 37°.

4 Take aliquots at times shown and dilute according to the following scheme. At each time, plate duplicate 0.1 ml samples on NA + thy plates.

Time (*min*)	Dilution
0	10^{-3}
10	10^{-3}
30	10^{-3}
50	10^{-3}
70	5 × 10^{-2} (0.2 into 10; 1 into 9)
90	10^{-2}
120	10^{-2}
150	10^{-1}

5 Incubate plates overnight.

Day following Part 1

Part 2   **1** Count the number of colonies on each plate and
1½ hr   calculate the viable cell concentration at each time
             of assay.

         2 Plot viable cell count against time on log-linear
             paper.

Experiment 9
Transformation

Background

A few species of bacteria can undergo a genetic alteration simply by the uptake from the medium of molecules of DNA extracted from another strain of the same species that has an inheritable distinguishing feature. This effect, termed *transformation*, was discovered in 1928 by GRIFFITH who observed the acquisition of virulence by an avirulent strain of a pneumococcus after exposure to heat-killed cells of the virulent form. AVERY, MCLEOD & MCCARTY (1944) later showed that the active agent in transformation is chemically-pure DNA. Transformation still provides the most convincing evidence that genetic information is carried by DNA rather than by protein. There has been a recent resurgence of interest in the complex processes involved in transformation because it offers a relatively direct way of studying the processes of recombination.

The events between the addition of the DNA to a bacterial culture and the expression of the newly-acquired genetic trait can be divided into four stages:

1 The DNA is absorbed by the cell. At this time it can still be removed by washing and can be inactivated by the addition of the enzyme deoxyribonuclease (DNase) to the culture.

2 The absorbed DNA becomes irreversibly bound. It is no longer susceptible to DNase in the medium.

3 The DNA begins the process of integration—the so-called 'eclipse phase' because little active transforming DNA can be isolated with the DNA of the recipient. (This is not true of *Haemophilus*.)

4 Part of the donor DNA, possibly only one strand, is integrated, probably by substitution, into the genome of the recipient.

The three species in which transformation is well established are *Streptococcus pneumoniae* (in U.S., *Diplococcus pneumoniae*), *Haemophilus influenzae* and *Bacillus subtilis*. Although under the best conditions a rather larger fraction of the recipient cells of the first two species can be transformed, *B.subtilis* is the most useful for student demonstration. This species, unlike the others, is nutritionally non-exacting, and will grow well

in a simple, defined medium. It is, therefore, possible to use a wide range
of mutants with simple auxotrophic markers. In contrast, the first two
transformation systems involve rather complicated growth requirements
and drug resistances are the only convenient markers.

References
ANAGNOSTOPOULOS C. & J.SPIZIZEN (1961) *J. Bact.* **81**, 741.
AVERY O.T., C.M.McLEOD & M.McCARTY (1944) *J. exp. Med.* **79**, 137.
GRIFFITH F. (1928) *J. Hyg.* **27**, 113.
RAVIN A.W. (1961) *Adv. Genet.* **10**, 61.
SPIZIZEN, J., B. E. REILLY & A. H. EVANS (1966) *Ann. Rev. Microbiol.*,
    20, 371.

Intention

The experiment utilizes a doubly auxotrophic strain of *B.subtilis* requiring
indole and tyrosine (ind^-tyr^-), in which the two mutational sites are
closely linked. Transformation of either or both of these genes can be
observed by selection for independence of either or both nutritional
requirements. The experiment is designed to demonstrate three points:
1. *Efficiency of transformation.* Approximately 1 in 1000 recipient
bacteria can be transformed to independence of a given growth requirement.
2. *Susceptibility to DNase.* The addition of DNase to the culture destroys
the transforming activity of the DNA if added early, but not if added
late in the experiment.
3. *Genetic linkage.* The separation and purification of transforming DNA
from bacteria leads to the breakdown of the bacterial genome into fragments. These are, however, large compared to the size of a gene, and the
closer two genes (markers) are linked genetically the greater is the chance
that they will remain on the same fragment of DNA. Over a wide range of
DNA concentrations, the number of cells transformed for a single marker
is a simple linear function of the concentration. To obtain double transformation of two *unlinked* markers, two separate molecules must be taken
up and the chance of double transformation is therefore proportional to
the square of the concentration. At a fixed low concentration of DNA, the
frequency of double transformants will therefore be only a small fraction
of the cells transformed for a single marker. If the markers are sufficiently
near one another to be found frequently on a single fragment of DNA,
then the frequency of co-transformation is close to that of transformation
for a single marker, while the frequency of double transformants falls off
at the same rate as that of transformants for each marker separately,

with decreasing DNA concentration. The markers are then referred to as linked markers.

In this experiment, the indole and tyrosine markers are sufficiently close for some 70% of the *ind⁻tyr⁻* cells transformed for one marker to be transformed for the other by DNA from an *ind⁺tyr⁺* strain. On the other hand, if DNA from an *ind⁺tyr⁻* strain is mixed with DNA from an *ind⁻tyr⁺* strain to give the same final concentration, so that the *ind⁺* and *tyr⁺* genes are necessarily on separate molecules, the frequency of double transformation to *ind⁺tyr⁺* is about 5% of the frequency of transformation for a single marker of *ind⁺* or *tyr⁺*.

The experiment requires two preliminary operations, the isolation of transforming DNA and the preparation of 'competent' cultures. The DNA isolated from two or three grams of cells provides sufficient material for many transformation experiments and retains its activity for long periods if kept sterile. It need not, therefore, be prepared for each experiment and can be provided as a reagent from a previously prepared stock.

B.subtilis is transformed at high frequency only if subjected to a special regime which produces cells said to be 'competent'. Competent cultures are rather tricky to prepare and some trial and error may be necessary in each laboratory before the best method is achieved.

DNA Extraction

Grow one litre of the appropriate strain of *B.subtilis* with vigorous aeration, either by bubbling or rapid shaking, in nutrient broth to about 5×10^8 cells/ml, harvest by centrifugation and wash in cold (4°) saline (0.14 M). Resuspend the pellet in 40 ml of cold saline (0.14 M NaCl) containing 0.001 M EDTA, per gram wet weight of packed cells*, and ensure that the pellet is well dispersed. Add 0.2 mg/ml of crystalline lysozyme and incubate with gentle shaking at 37°. After 5 to 10 min the cells lyse and the suspension clears but becomes very viscous. Add an equal volume of 90% phenol. [It is preferable to use freshly-distilled phenol and it is imperative that immediately before use the phenol is shaken twice with buffer (0.1 M borate) to remove traces of acid.] Shake gently for 20 min to keep the phases well-dispersed. Spin at 5000 rpm for 5 min. Remove as much as possible of the aqueous (top) layer containing the DNA, without disturbing the interface at which the denatured protein accumulates. Remove the dissolved phenol from the aqueous layer either by shaking twice for 1 min with 4 ml of ether in a separating funnel or, if possible, by dialysis overnight against a large volume (2L or more) of saline-EDTA. A second centrifugation (20 min at 10,000 rpm) is usually

---

* The wet weight of cells from 1 litre of culture at 5×10^8 cells/ml is approximately 1 g.

necessary to remove residual denatured protein. The DNA is then pre-
cipitated by adding an equal volume of 2-ethoxy-ethanol slowly down
the side of the tube and swirling the beaker; the fibres of DNA are
removed by winding them on a glass rod. Wash the fibres once with
alcohol, press dry with filter paper and redissolve in one-third the original
volume (13 ml for about 1 g wet weight of original cells) of 0.01 M NaCl
and 0.001 M EDTA and leave overnight.

Determine the DNA concentration. The optical density of native DNA
is approximately 20 (at 260 mμ) for 1 mg/ml. Adjust the concentration to
between 1.5 and 2 mg/ml, and then add one-tenth volume of 1 M NaCl.
If the solution is at all turbid, precipitate the denatured protein by spin-
ning at 10,000 rpm for 20 min. This preparation should be stored at 4°.

Competent Cultures

Inoculate the growth medium (Subtilis Minimal Medium—SMM;
Appendix A19) supplemented with 20 μg/ml indole and 10 μg/ml tyrosine,
with a single colony of the recipient strain and aerate gently overnight.
Dilute into fresh SMM to give an optical density, at 450 mμ, of 0.8
optical density (od) units (in 1 cm cells). Aerate *very vigorously* (by
bubbling). Follow the od at half-hourly intervals. It should increase at
about 0.4 od units per hour. After about 3 hours, as the optical density
reaches 1.7–1.8, the rate of increase should decline and when it reaches
0.2 od units per hour, dilute with an equal volume of pre-warmed
'starvation' medium (SMS + 0.5% glucose without other supplements;
Appendix A18). Continue the vigorous aeration for 90 min. The culture
should now be maximally competent and remain so for about another
hour. At the expense of perhaps 80% of the competent cells, these cultures can be kept at −20° for a week in 15% glycerol. Add 1.5 ml of
glycerol per 9 ml of culture and dispense in 0.9 ml aliquots and freeze
quickly.

Requirements

Part 1 (*per class of 20 groups*)

Three solutions of DNA at a concentration of 100 μg/ml.

> 3 ml DNA *A*: DNA extracted from the proto-trophic strain EMG50 (*ind⁺tyr⁺*).
>
> 2 ml DNA *B*: DNA extracted from an indole-requiring strain EMG51 (*ind⁻tyr⁺*).
>
> 2 ml DNA *C*: DNA extracted from a tyrosine-requiring strain EMG52 (*ind⁺tyr⁻*).

5 ml DNase soln; containing 400 μg/ml DNase dissolved in 0.2 *M* MgSO$_4$.

Per group

5 ml of competent culture of strain EMG53 (*ind⁻tyr⁻*) containing about 10^7 cells/ml.

6 plates of subtilis minimal agar (SMA; Appendix A20).

8 plates of SMA + 10 μg/ml tyrosine (SMA +tyr).

8 plates of SMA + 20 μg/ml indole (SMA + ind).

2 plates of SMA + 10 μg/ml tyrosine + 20 μg/ml indole (SMA + tyr + ind).

200 ml buffer.

4 small tubes.

10 large tubes.

Method

Part 1
1½–2 hr

1 Prepare 20 dilution tubes (2 × 10 ml; 18 × 9 ml). Label the small tubes *A* to *D*, and place in 37° waterbath.

Label SMA plates (3,4,15,16,17 and 18).

Label SMA + tyr plates (1,5,6,7,11,19,20 and 21).

Label SMA + ind plates (2,8,9,10,12,22,23 and 24).

Label SMA + tyr + ind plates (13 and 14).

2 Follow protocol below.

Time (min)	Tube A	B	C	D
0	Add 0.05 ml DNA A + 0.05 ml DNase	Add 0.05 ml DNA A	Add 0.1 ml buffer	Add 0.05 ml of a 1 : 1 mixture of DNAs $B + C$
15	Add 0.9 ml competent culture	Add 0.9 ml competent culture	Add 0.9 ml competent culture	Add 0.9 ml competent culture
35	—	Add 0.05 ml DNase	—	Add 0.05 ml DNase
45 Plate and dilute	Spread 0.2 ml samples on: (i) SMA + tyr at 10^0 diln Plate (1) (ii) SMA + ind at 10^0 diln Plate (2)	Spread 0.2 ml samples on: (i) SMA at 10^{-1} and 10^{-2} dilns Plates (3) & (4) (ii) SMA + tyr at 10^{-1}, 10^{-2} 10^{-3} dilns Plates (5),(6),(7) (iii) SMA + ind at 10^{-1}, 10^{-2} and 10^{-3} dilns Plates (8),(9),(10)	Spread 0.2 ml samples on: (i) SMA + tyr at 10^0 diln Plate (11) (ii) SMA + ind at 10^0 diln Plate (12) (iii) SMA + ind + tyr at 10^{-5} and 10^{-6} dilns Plates (13) & (14)	Spread 0.2 ml samples on: (i) SMA at 10^0, 10^{-1}, 10^{-2} and 10^{-3} dilns Plates (15) to (18) (ii) SMA + tyr at 10^{-1}, 10^{-2} and 10^{-3} dilns Plates (19) to (21) (iii) SMA + ind at 10^{-1}, 10^{-2} and 10^{-3} dilns Plates (22) to (24)

3 Incubate all plates for 48 hr.

Two days following Part 1

Part 2
$1-1\frac{1}{2}$ hr   Count colonies, record and interpret results.

Experiment 10
DNA-RNA hybridization

Background

The demonstration by DOTY, MARMUR, EIGNER and SCHILDKRAUT (1960) that the two strands of the DNA double helix can be separated, and that new double helices can be reconstituted with the restoration of base pairing has had far-reaching consequences in molecular biology. For two DNA strands to pair they must have substantial sequences of bases complementary to one another. If two DNAs from different organisms have sufficient regions of homology, these can pair and the formation of new, hybrid, double helices can be detected. The extent of the formation of such hybrids (hybridization) is therefore an indication of the degree to which these organisms are phylogenetically related. Hybridization between DNAs from different species is now a useful taxonomic tool.

Similarly, if there are sequences of bases in an RNA molecule that correspond to sequences in one or other of the DNA strands, these too should be capable of forming hybrid DNA-RNA double helices. The detection of such hybrids was achieved simultaneously in a number of laboratories and the analysis of these hybrids has given valuable confirmation of a number of hypotheses concerning the relationships between DNA and RNA. Among the most noteworthy findings are that both transfer- and ribosomal-RNAs, as well as messenger-RNA, are synthesized on a DNA template, and that messenger-RNA is complementary to only one strand of the DNA double helix. It is a technique which is now being exploited widely to elucidate the factors determining gene expression.

The best way of separating the two strands of the DNA double helix is by heating solutions of low ionic strength—a process referred to as 'melting'. The optimal conditions for reassembling double helical structures (often called 'reannealing') are obtained by holding solutions of high ionic strength at a temperature somewhat below the 'melting temperature', but high enough for many hydrogen bonds to be labile. In practice, temperatures between 60 and 70° are best for the pairing process.

That *new* double helices are formed under these conditions has been demonstrated by a number of techniques, most convincingly by caesium chloride (CsCl) density-gradient experiments. A striking consequence of hybrid formation between DNA and RNA is that the bound RNA is markedly more resistant to RNase than is free RNA, and the enzyme-resistant fraction has been used as a measure of the amount of RNA complexed with DNA. Both these experiments and particularly the density-gradient experiment are rather elaborate, so that the development by NYGAARD & HALL (1964) of a quick and relatively easy method of analyzing the amount of RNA complexed with DNA was a most useful advance. The method relies on the fact that certain nitrocellulose filter membranes retain DNA and DNA-RNA hybrid molecules, but not molecules of free RNA. If the RNA carries a radioactive label, measurement of the radio-activity retained by the filter can be related to the amount of RNA and DNA that can form complexes.

References
DOTY P. (1960) *Harvey Lectures* **55**, 103.
DOTY P., J.MARMUR, J.EIGNER & C.SCHILDKRAUT (1960) *Proc. Nat. Acad. Sci., Wash.*, **46**, 461.
GILLESPIE D. & S.SPIEGELMAN (1965) *J. Mol. Biol.*, **12**, 829.
MARMUR J., R.ROWND & C.SCHILDKRAUT (1963) In: *Progress in Nucleic Acid Research*, **1**, 231.
NYGAARD A.P. & B.D.HALL (1964) *J. Mol. Biol.*, **9**, 125.
SPIEGELMAN S. & M.HAYASHI (1963) *Cold. Spr. Harb. Symp. quant. Biol.*, **28**, 161. (A number of other papers in this symposium are very relevant to this topic and are well worth reading.)

Intention

The experiment given here is based on the experiments of Nygaard and Hall and concerns the degree of homology between messenger-RNA made after infection with phage T4, and DNA from the phage. RNA similarly prepared from uninfected cells is used as control. As with the transformation experiment (Experiment 9, p.46), this experiment requires a substantial degree of pre-preparation, but both the RNA and DNA, if sterile, can be kept for long periods so that other and more elaborate experiments can easily be devised and performed.

Preparation of phage DNA

Inoculate 1 litre of phage broth with 50 ml overnight culture of *E.coli B* (EMG31) and aerate vigorously at 37°. When the cell density reaches 4×10^8 bacteria/ml, add a total of 10^{10} T4 phage particles. Aerate vigorously for a further 4 hr at 37°, and then add 1 ml chloroform and leave in the cold (4°) overnight. Remove the bacterial debris by centrifuging at 5000 rpm for 5 min. Then centrifuge at 15,000 rpm for one hour and carefully discard the supernatant. Cover the precipitates (pellets) with a total of 20 ml of phage buffer and leave overnight at 4°. *Gently* resuspend the pellets and spin at 5000 rpm for 10 min to remove bacterial debris. Decant the supernatant and assay for viable phage. Then dilute to 10^{12} particles/ml with phage buffer.

To prepare the DNA, shake the phage suspension gently with an equal volume of buffer-saturated phenol, and then treat as for transforming DNA (see Experiment 9, p.48).

Preparation of labelled RNA

Inoculate 5 ml of an overnight culture of *E.coli B* (EMG31) into 100 ml phage broth, as in the previous preparation, and aerate vigorously at 37°. When the cell count is 2×10^8 bacteria/ml, centrifuge for 5 min at 3000 rpm, pour off the supernatant and resuspend the pellet in 10 ml of phage buffer. Add a total of 10^{11} T4 phage particles and, after 10 min to allow adsorption, dilute into 100 ml phage broth at 37°, containing 1 μg/ml of radioactive uridine ($\sim$ 20 mC/mMole if C^{14}) and aerate vigorously at 37°. After a further 10 min, chill by pouring on to ice, spin in the cold at 5000 rpm for 5 min, discard the supernatant and resuspend the pellet in 2 ml buffer (0.1 M Mg acetate, 0.06 M KCl, 0.01 M TRIS, pH 7.3). *Freeze* quickly in a deep freeze. To lyse, *thaw* by stirring in waterbath at 50° for 5 min. Add 0.5 ml of 0.1 N acetic acid. Shake with an equal volume of 90% phenol (see note in Experiment 9, p.48) in water bath at 60° for 5 min. Chill rapidly, spin at 5000 rpm for 5 min and re-extract the aqueous layer in the same way. Remove the phenol from the aqueous layer with ether (1 vol) and add 2 vol of ethanol. Stir and spool out any DNA fibres. The RNA precipitate is amorphous: collect this precipitate by centrifugation. Redissolve the RNA in 0.01 M KCl. Pass this solution down a 10 × 1 cm column of Sephadex G25 (Pharmacia, Ltd., see Appdx. L), equilibrated with 0.07 M potassium acetate-acetic acid buffer (pH 5.2) by pouring through until the pH of the effluent is 5.2. Collect the eluate containing the RNA, determined from the optical density at 260 mμ. Add one quarter volume of 2 M KCl, and adjust to pH 7.3. Filter through a membrane filter (1 fresh membrane is required per mg RNA) to remove nonspecific, radioactive material that absorbs to the filter.

Repeat this preparation omitting the phage infection as the RNA control from uninfected cells.

Denaturation of DNA
Dilute DNA to 200 μg/ml with distilled water, and then adjust the final concentration of the solvent to be approximately 0.05 M KCl and 0.01 M TRIS pH 7.3. Heat for 15 min in boiling water; plunge into ice.

Requirements

> 8 membrane filters. (Type B6 coarse, Schleicher & Schuell; see Appendix L).
> 1 membrane-filter holder.
> 1 Buchner flask.
> 8 counting vials or planchettes.
> 1 waterbath at 67°–70°.
> 8 small tubes.
> 500 ml of solvent—0.5 M KCl, 0.01 M TRIS pH 7.3.
> 0.5 ml containing 1 od unit/ml at 260 mμ of RNA 1 (from T4-infected cells).
> 0.5 ml containing 1 od unit/ml of RNA 2 (from uninfected cells).
> 1 ml containing 0.3 od unit/ml of DNA from phage T4 denatured by the method given above.

55

Method

6 hr   1 Put filters to soak in 50 ml of 0.5 *M* KCl and occasionally agitate.

2 Mark tubes 1–8. Add to each 1 ml of solvent.

3 Add 0.1 ml of the DNA solution to tube 2,3,4,6,7 and 8.

4 Add to tube 1   0.1 ml of RNA 1
              2   0.05 ml of RNA 1
              3   0.1 ml of RNA 1
              4   0.2 ml of RNA 1
              5   0.1 ml of RNA 2
              6   0.05 ml of RNA 2
              7   0.1 ml of RNA 2
              8   0.1 ml of RNA 2.

5 Incubate for 2 hr at 67°–70°.

6 Pour the contents of each tube into 10 ml of solvent.

7 Wash each membrane with 5 ml of solvent, filter the dilute DNA-RNA mixture and wash with 5 × 10 ml of solvent.

8 Remove membrane and dry.

9 Count radioactivity

10 Determine the homology with phage DNA of the rapidly-labelled RNA from infected and uninfected cells.

Note. More extensive experiments of this kind can be set up to test the validity of this conclusion and the effects of varying the conditions of the experiment (see NYGAARD and HALL, 1964). This type of experiment has a number of possible variations, as for example, measurement of the homology of the RNA in *E. coli* K12 (λ) bacteria with phage λDNA, before and after induction of λ phage development.

Experiments 11 and 12
The control and expression of related genes in the *lac* operon

Background

In addition to the mediation of synthetic (anabolic) reactions as shown in experiments 2,4,5,6 and 7, enzymes also control those reactions which lead to the breakdown of compounds (catabolism) in order that the cell may obtain energy and a source of carbon groups which can be used in anabolic reactions. As was found for the synthetic reactions (see Expt. 2), mutants which are unable to perform one or other of these catabolic steps can be isolated. For example, the 'wild-type' strain of *Escherichia coli* can break down (or ferment) a range of sugars, and mutants can be selected which have lost the ability to ferment one or more of these sugars.

The following experiments make use of mutants which are unable to ferment lactose, a disaccharide of glucose and galactose. They have been designed to illustrate the controlled transfer of genetic information from genes into enzymatically-active proteins, and for this purpose, mutants in three distinct *lactose* (*lac*) genes will be used. The '*y*' gene specifies the structure of a permease-enzyme which is responsible for the accumulation of lactose in the cell. The '*z*' gene specifies the structure of an enzyme (*β-galactosidase*) which hydrolyses (breaks down) lactose and other β-galactosides. The third gene, the '*i*' gene, is a regulator gene, which controls the synthesis of a diffusible product which is thought to act on a fourth gene ('*o*' gene) called the operator gene, and thereby regulate the enzyme synthesis of the two structural genes, *y* and *z*. Mutants affecting these various genes involved in lactose fermentation are located close together on the *E.coli* chromosome. In the i^+ condition of the *i* gene, the gene product permits the expression of the *z* and *y* genes (i.e. the synthesis of their enzyme products) *only* in the presence of an inducer such as lactose or another β-galactoside. Thus, mutation to the i^- condition gives rise to cells which are said to be 'constitutive', in that the expression of the *z* and *y* genes is permitted *even in the absence of an added inducer*. The genes *z,y* together with the operator gene *o*, form a coordinate unit of function which is termed an 'operon' (see JACOB & MONOD 1961).

The essential requirement for enzymological work is a convenient and reliable assay procedure. Relatively few enzymes have the stability and convenience of assay which make β-galactosidase the system of choice for many kinds of experiment. The assay procedure which is used in the two following experiments is based on that described by PARDEE, JACOB & MONOD (1959) in which a colourless substrate (*o*-nitrophenyl-β-galactoside, ONPG) is hydrolysed by the enzyme to give the coloured product *o*-nitrophenol (ONP).

$$\text{ONPG} \xrightarrow{\text{β-galactosidase}} \text{Galactose} + \text{ONP (yellow)}$$

The amount of yellow colour, and therefore the amount of hydrolysis, is conveniently assayed spectrophotometrically.

References
AMES B.N. & R.G.MARTIN (1964) *Ann. Rev. Biochem.* **33**, 237.
BECKWITH J. (1964) *Biochim. Biophys. Acta.* **76**, 162.
BENZER S. & S.P.CHAMPE (1961) *Proc. Nat. Acad. Sci., Wash.*, **47**, 1025.
JACOB F. & J.MONOD, (1961) *J. Mol. Biol.*, **3**, 318.
JACOB F. & J.MONOD (1965) *Biochem. Biophys. Res. Comm.* **18**, 693.
NAKADA D. & B.MAGASANIK (1964) *J. Mol. Biol.* **8**, 105.
PARDEE A.B., F.JACOB & J.MONOD (1959) *J. Mol. Biol.* **1**, 165.

Procedure for assay of β-galactosidase

1. Reagents
ONPG. Dissolve 0.2 g ONPG in 50 ml of 0.25 *M* sodium phosphate buffer at pH 7.0 containing 0.001 *M* MgSO$_4$, 0.0002 *M* MnSO$_4$ and 0.1 *M* mercaptoethanol. Heat as little as possible to dissolve the ONPG and cool immediately. Store the reagent in a refrigerator.
1 *M* solution of Na$_2$CO$_3$
Toluene.

2. Method of assay
Shortly before taking samples, place a series of small tubes, each containing one drop of toluene (use same pipette throughout the experiment), in an ice bath where they are maintained until the entire series has been taken. At the time of sampling, add 1 ml of bacterial culture to each tube, shake vigorously and return to the ice bath. When all the samples have been

collected, the tubes are placed in a water bath at 37° for 30 min and shaken at intervals throughout this period. They are then transferred to a 28° water bath and 0.2 ml of ONPG reagent is added to each of the tubes. The addition of ONPG is timed at intervals of fifteen seconds, and hydrolysis of ONPG which then occurs is allowed to proceed until a visible yellow colour is produced (usually 15–30 min is adequate). The reaction is stopped by the addition of 0.5 ml of 1 M Na$_2$CO$_3$ solution to the tubes, again at 15 sec intervals. The exact time interval between starting and stopping the reaction is noted. (The function of the Na$_2$CO$_3$ is to raise the pH sufficiently so as to stop the reaction and enhance the colour due to the o-nitrophenyl ion.) The optical density of each of the tubes is then compared in a spectrophotometer using a blank containing no enzyme, at 420 mμ and 550 mμ. (The 550 mμ reading is used to correct for absorption due to bacterial turbidity.) Enzyme activity (e) in units per ml can then be calculated from the expression

$$e = \frac{OD_{420} - (1.65 \times OD_{550})}{\text{time incub (min)} \times 0.0075}$$

Experiment 11
Phenotypic behaviour of *lac* mutants

Intention

This experiment demonstrates the phenotypic behaviour of a number of the mutants of the *lac* region following growth in media with or without either glucose, thiomethylgalactoside (TMG) or isopropylthiogalactoside (IPTG). Either TMG or IPTG act as inducers for the lactose genes but glucose does not induce. Genetic studies show that these *lac* mutants have sites which map closely together in the lactose region of the *E.coli* chromosome.

The four mutants required are EMG7 ($i^+z^+y^+$), EMG8 ($i^+z^-y^+$), EMG9 ($i^-z^+y^+$) and EMG10 ($i^+z^+y^-$) (see Appendix B). These strains are grown on nutrient agar (NA) plates (stock plates) and then each is inoculated in M9-glycerol medium (M9 medium in which 0.2% w/v glycerol replaces glucose), supplemented with the appropriate growth factors, and incubated overnight. (The necessary supplements are: EMG7—thiamin; EMG8—thiamin; EMG9—thiamin; EMG10—thiamin, threonine and leucine).

Requirements

Part 1   1 ml o/n cultures of strains EMG7,8,9 and 10 in M9-glycerol medium (Appendix A13)

6 ml ONPG solution ⎫
15 ml 1 M Na$_2$CO$_3$ ⎭ Reagents for assay

1 ml TMG solution (2×10^{-2} M) ⎫
1 ml IPTG solution (5×10^{-3} M) ⎬ Supplements
1 ml glucose solution (2% w/v) ⎭

Ice bath

2 waterbaths set at 37° and 28°

Spectrophotometer

20 large tubes each containing 5 ml M9-glycerol medium plus leucine, threonine and thiamin (each at 20 mg/ml.)

20 Pasteur pipettes (for bubbling cultures)
20 large tubes for assay of β-galactosidase.

Method

Part 1
6–7 hr
(with intervals)

1 Five replicate sub-cultures of each strain are prepared by inoculating 5 ml sterile M9-glycerol medium with 0.05 ml of each overnight culture. Using Pasteur pipettes, and a small aeration pump, aerate each culture at 37°* until a concentration of $c.2 \times 10^8$/ml is achieved (3–4 hr).

2 Add to each tube, as specified by the protocol below, and where required, supplements of 0.55 ml TMG (to $c.2 \times 10^{-3}$ M), 0.6 ml IPTG (to $c.5 \times 10^{-4}$ M) and 0.6 ml glucose (to $c.0.02\%$ w/v).

Mutant Supplement	$i^+z^+y^+$ (EMG 7)	$i^+z^-y^+$ (EMG 8)	$i^-z^+y^+$ (EMG 9)	$i^+z^+y^-$ (EMG 10)
Nil				
TMG				
TMG + glucose				
IPTG				
IPTG + glucose				

3 Continue the incubation and aeration for a further 45 min.

4 At the conclusion of the 45 min incubation, remove 1 ml samples from each culture and assay for β-galactosidase activity as previously detailed (p.58).

5 Record your data as in the Table above.

Explain your results in terms of the known genotype of the organisms. Note the inhibitory effect of glucose on the synthesis of β-galactosidase [see AMES, B.N. & R.G.MARTIN (1964) *Ann. Rev. Biochem.* **33**, 237].

* Alternatively, aerate in Erlenmeyer flasks on rotary shaker.

Experiment 12
Gene expression in the *lac* region following genetic transfer

Intention

This experiment demonstrates the appearance and accumulation of the products of two genes of the lactose region of *E.coli*, following their transfer from a male strain into a female strain of *E.coli* K12. The experiment utilizes a male 'intermediate' strain harbouring a 'substituted' sex-factor (F-prime factor) carrying the lactose region (F'-*lac*), which is infectiously transferred at high efficiency to females on contact (see p.130 and Expts. 31 and 32). The infected female cells can thus be made heterozygous for the *lac* region and complementation in this region can thereby be studied. In this experiment, the male transfers an F-prime factor carrying the lactose genes i^+z^+ into a female which is genetically i^-z^-. The appearance in this female of the dominant i^+ and z^+ activities can thus be detected. The z^+ gene expresses itself in the structure of the enzyme β-galactosidase, whereas the i^+ gene product, after an initial delay, represses the synthesis of this enzyme, except when an inducer is present.

As a prelude to the experiments the male strain EMG11 [F'-*lac*$^+(i^+z^+)$] and the female strain EMG12 [*lac*$^-$ (i^-z^-)F$^-$] should be cultured overnight, each in 5 ml M9-glycerol medium (p.60).

Requirements

1ml o/n cultures of EMG11 and 12 in M9 + glycerol.
60 ml M9-glycerol medium.
5 × 250 ml sterile Erlenmeyer flasks.
43 large tubes.
0.2 ml chloramphenicol solution (CM)—2.5 mg/ml.
0.2 ml 5-fluorouracil solution (FU)—2 mg/ml.
0.2 ml thymidine solution (TDN)—4 mg/ml.
10 ml ONPG reagent.
25 ml 1 M Na_2CO_3 solution.
4 ml TMG solution (2×10^{-2} M).
Ice bath.
Water baths set at 37° and 28°.
Spectrophotometer.

Method

6 hr	**1** Sub-culture from the o/n cultures of the two strains provided into M9-glycerol medium by transferring 0.4 ml of EMG12 (*lac⁻*F⁻) to 40 ml medium (label this flask *A*) and 0.2 ml of EMG11 (F'-*lac⁺*) to 20 ml medium (label this flask *B*).

Time (min) —90   **2** Incubate sub-cultures at 37° in waterbath with aeration by shaking until a concentration of about 2×10^8 cells/ml is reached (about $1\frac{1}{2}$ hr).

0   **3** Mix 36 ml from *A* and 18 ml from *B* into a sterile flask—(label this flask *C*).

Continue incubation of all three flasks, but withdraw aeration which would otherwise prevent conjugation.

0   Take 0.5 ml from *A* to enzyme-assay tube.* Label *A*0.

Take 0.5 ml from *B* to assay tube. Label *B*0.

Take 1.0 ml from *C* to assay tube. Label *C*0.

5   Take 1.0 ml from *C* to assay tube. Label *C*5.

10   Take 1.0 ml from *C* to assay tube. Label *C*10.

15   Take 1.0 ml from *C* to assay tube. Label *C*15.

20   Take 1.0 ml from *C* to assay tube. Label *C*20.

Gently remove 16 ml from *C* into a flask. Label *D*. Add 0.16 ml CM. Incubate *D* at 37°.

Gently remove 16 ml from *C* into a flask. Label *E*. Add 0.16 ml FU + 0.16 ml TDN. Incubate *E* at 37°.

30   Take 1 ml from flasks *C*, *D*, and *E* each into an assay tube. Label *C*30, *D*30, *E*30.

Take 0.5 ml from *A* and *B* each to assay tube. Label *A*30, *B*30.

40   Take 1 ml from *C*, *D*, and *E* each to assay tube. Label *C*40, *D*40, *E*40.

60   Take 1 ml from *C*, *D*, and *E* to assay tube. Label *C*60, *D*60, *E*60.

Take 0.5 ml from *A* and *B* to assay tube. Label *A*60, *B*60.

80   Take 1 ml from *C*, *D*, and *E* to assay tube. Label *C*80, *D*80, *E*80.

* Large tube containing one drop of toluene in ice bath.

Time (min)

100   Take 1 ml from *C*, *D*, and *E* to assay tube. Label *C*100, *D*100, *E*100.

120   Take 1 ml from *C*, *D*, and *E* to assay tube. Label *C*120, *D*120, *E*120.

Take 0.5 ml from *A* and *B* to assay tube. Label *A*120, *B*120.

Add TMG; 1.2 ml to *C*, 1.1 ml to *D*, 1.1 ml to *E*.

140   Take 1 ml from *C*, *D*, and *E* to assay tube. Label *C*140, *D*140, *E*140.

160   Take 1 ml from *C*, *D*, and *E* to assay tube. Label *C*160, *D*160, *E*160.

180   Take 1 ml from *C*, *D*, and *E* to assay tube. Label *C*180, *D*180, *E*180.

4 Now assay all samples for β-galactosidase (see p.58).

5 Plot your results against time after mixing.

Conclusions

Note that:

1. Enzyme synthesis in the first part of the experiment is dependent on gene transfer (compare parental controls *A* and *B* with mixed-culture curves, *C*, *D*, and *E*).

2. The inhibition of synthesis by chloramphenicol and fluorouracil is not relieved by addition of the inducer TMG (curves *D* and *E*).

3. Enzyme synthesis stops (curve *C*) after 80–90 min due to the accumulation of an intracelluar inhibitor. The activity of this intracellular inhibitor is removed by the addition of inducer TMG (curve *C*). The inhibitor could be demonstrated to be a product of the *i* gene by using an *F'-lac⁻* donor strain carrying the genes i^-z^+, in which case enzyme synthesis would continue linearly beyond 90 min.

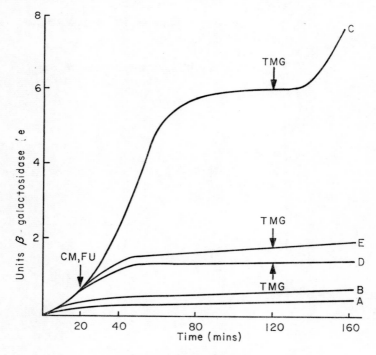

Fig.4 Kinetics of transfer of *lac* genes

If facilities exist to deal with, and count, radioactive isotopes, the experiment could be extended by following the incorporation of labelled amino acids, e.g. L-leucine labelled either with ^{3}H or ^{14}C, during the experiment.

In this case it will be found that only CM prevents net incorporation of label. FU inhibits enzyme synthesis by virtue of its incorporation into messenger-RNA in place of uracil, thus giving an incorrect message to the protein-synthesizing machinery of the cell [BENZER S. & S. P. CHAMPE (1961) *Proc. Nat. Acad. Sci., Wash.*, **47**, 1025].

Experiments 13 to 18
Experiments with 'virulent' bacteriophages

Introduction

The following experiments have been designed to acquaint the student with some of the main techniques used in research with virulent phage. Most experiments will be performed with the two closely-related phages T2 and T4, which have as their host bacterium *Escherichia coli* strain *B*.

Standard assay for bacteriophage

The method used in these experiments is the agar-layer method detailed on p.6.

Overnight Cultures

Unless specifically stated otherwise (cf. Experiment 15), all overnight cultures in this section are prepared by inoculating into 10 ml of phage-broth (Appendix A15) contained in a large tube and incubating overnight at 37° without aeration.

Preparation of host bacteria

In most experiments phage growth is followed in cultures of bacteria which are in the log. phase of growth. These are prepared by diluting an o/n broth culture 100-fold into fresh phage broth and aerating gently for about $2\frac{1}{2}$ hr at 37° so as to give a concentration of about 10^8 cells/ml. These cells are then centrifuged at low speed and resuspended in fresh broth at the required cell density. When desired, cyanide is then added to the suspension (see below).

Synchronous adsorption of bacteriophage

In many phage experiments it is essential to have a population of infected cells in each of which phage development has proceeded for the same length of time. Since phage growth depends on bacterial metabolism, the simplest method of achieving this is to adsorb the phage particles to bacteria which are temporarily non-metabolizing due to some imposed inhibition, and then to start phage development synchronously in all infected cells by suddenly releasing the inhibition. A convenient inhibitor is cyanide; the presence of concentrations of $M/500$ (conveniently by the addition of 0.04 M solution of KCN) completely arrests phage development without interfering with adsorption, and a subsequent dilution at 10^{-4} removes all effects of the drug.

General reference books

ADAMS M.H. (1959) *Bacteriophages*, Interscience: New York.

HAYES W. (1968) *The Genetics of Bacteria and their Viruses* (Second Edition), Blackwell Scientific Publications: Oxford.

LURIA S.E. (1953) *General Virology*, pp.157–208, John Wiley: New York.

STENT G.S. (1963) *Molecular Biology of Bacterial Viruses*, W.H.Freeman: London.

General chemistry of phage infection

HERSHEY A.D. & M.CHASE (1952) *J. Gen. Physiol.* **36**, 39.

HERSHEY A.D., A.DIXON & M.CHASE (1953) *J. Gen. Physiol.* **36**, 777.

HERSHEY A.D. (1953) *J. Gen. Physiol.* **37**, 1.

HERSHEY A.D. & N.MELECHEN (1957) *Virology* **3**, 207.

HERSHEY A.D. (1957) *Advanc. Virus Res.* **4**, 25.

Phage genetics

CHASE M. & A.D.DOERMANN (1958) *Genetics* **43**, 332.

HERSHEY A.D. (1958) *Cold Spr. Harb. Symp. Quant. Biol.* **23**, 19.

LEVINTHAL C. (1959) In *The Viruses*, **2**. Eds F.M.Burnett & W.M. Stanley. Academic Press: London & New York.

VISCONTI N. & M.DELBRÜCK (1953) *Genetics* **38**, 5.

Experiment 13
Adsorption of phage to bacteria

Background

Adsorption of phage to bacteria occurs as a result of random collisions, so that the rate of adsorption depends both on the bacterial and the phage concentrations. When phage and bacteria are mixed, the following classes are present:
1. unadsorbed phage
2. infected bacteria
3. uninfected bacteria.

By the following techniques it is possible to count the numbers in each of these classes, and so determine the extent to which the adsorption has occurred in a given time.

1. *Unadsorbed phage.* There are two simple methods for assaying these phage:

   (a) A sample of the adsorption mixture is shaken with a few drops of chloroform. The chloroform kills both infected and uninfected bacteria, but not free phage particles. Thus the only surviving class is unadsorbed phage.

   (b) If the host bacteria are streptomycin-sensitive, then the addition of streptomycin to the adsorption mixture kills both the infected and uninfected bacteria. Again the only surviving class is unadsorbed phage, which can be assayed using streptomycin-resistant indicator bacteria.

2. *Infected bacteria.* The addition of antiphage serum to the adsorption mixture will inactivate the unadsorbed phage. If the mixture is then plated with sensitive bacteria, all the plaques will arise from infected cells (*infected centres*).

3. *Uninfected bacteria.* These are estimated by plating the mixture on 'salt-free' medium, without the addition of indicator bacteria. Under these conditions, each of the uninfected bacteria produces a colony. The absence of salt in the medium precludes further phage adsorption, so preventing the further infection and lysis of these colonies by the phage particles also present in the mixture.

If there are more bacteria than phage in the adsorption mixture, then most of the cells that become infected will have adsorbed only one phage particle, and will therefore be 'singly-infected'. Also a large fraction of the bacteria will remain uninfected under these circumstances. If, on the other hand, there are more phage than bacteria in the adsorption mixture, most of the bacteria will become 'multiply-infected', and only a small fraction of the bacteria will remain uninfected and thus survive as colony formers. From a knowledge of the size of this surviving fraction, it is possible to calculate the average 'multiplicity of infection' in the adsorption mixture, i.e. the average number of phage particles adsorbed to each bacterium in the culture.

This calculation rests on two assumptions. First, that the adsorption of one phage to a bacterium does not influence the adsorption of a second, i.e. the phages are randomly distributed among the bacteria. Second, that all the bacteria have equal probability of adsorbing a phage particle. If these assumptions hold, then the phage will be distributed among the bacteria in accordance with the Poisson distribution, which is expressed in the following formula:

$$Pr = \frac{m^r e^{-m}}{r!}$$

Here Pr gives the fraction of bacteria which is infected by exactly r phages when the average multiplicity of infection is m. $Po = e^{-m}$ is therefore the fraction of uninfected bacteria in the culture; this number can be found experimentally, and from this the multiplicity m can be simply calculated. It will probably be useful for the student who is unfamiliar with the Poisson distribution to fill in at least part of the following table, by calculations from the formula.

r m	0	1	2	3	4	5	6	7	8	9	10	11	12
0.1	0.905			—	—	—	—	—	—	—	—	—	—
0.4	0.670				—	—	—	—	—	—	—	—	—
1.0	0.368					—	—	—	—	—	—	—	—
2.0	0.135									—	—	—	—
5.0	0.007												
10.0	0.00045												

Intention

The experiment is designed to show the adsorption of phage to sensitive host cells, and its inactivation by specific antiserum.

As a preliminary to the experiment, o/n cultures of strains EMG31 (*E.coli* B) and EMG32 (*E.coli* B/S; a streptomycin-resistant strain of *E.coli* B) in phage-broth are required. A preparation of T4 particles (see p.7, and a preparation of T4 antiserum (*K* value = 20, see Appendix H) should also be available.

Requirements

Part 1   *Host Bacteria*—1 ml log. culture of *E.coli* strain B (EMG31) in phage-broth (Appendix A15) containing M/500 KCN.

Indicator Bacteria—10 ml o/n phage-broth culture of *E.coli* B/S (EMG32).

0.5 ml T4 phage at 5 × 10⁹ particles/ml.

0.1 ml anti-T4 serum (*K* = 20).

10 T-phage nutrient agar (TNA) plates (Appendix A16).

2 Strep TNA plates (2000 μg streptomycin/ml).*

3 'salt-free' TNA plates (see footnote p.188).

50 ml soft agar (held molten at 46°) (Appendix A11).

Chloroform.

1 ml streptomycin solution (3% w/v).

150 ml buffer.

13 large tubes.

15 small tubes.

Method

Part 1   **1** Prepare: 13 dilution tubes (9 × 10 ml; 4 × 9 ml)
1 hr   15 small tubes of soft agar (keep in 46° waterbath).

2 Label plates (on back) as follows:
    10 TNA plates—numbers (1)–(10)
    2 Strep TNA plates—numbers (11)–(12)
    3 'salt-free' TNA plates—numbers (13)–(15).

---

* This concentration of streptomycin, added to prevent the formation of 'infected centres' from phage-infected bacteria will be abbreviated as '*Strep*'. (The concentration normally adequate to prevent complete growth of *str-s* bacteria is 200 μg/ml, which will be denoted by SM).

3 Put a tube containing 1 ml host bacteria (*adsorption tube*) in 37° waterbath and allow to equilibrate for about 10 min. During this time, assay both the bacteria and the T4 phage stock as follows.*

		Plates
Bacteria	0.2 ml of 10^{-5} dilution	(1) & (2)
Phage	0.3 ml of 10^{-7} dilution (+I)	(3) & (4)

Time (min)

0 Add 0.1 ml phage to host bacteria in adsorption tube at 37°.

6 Dilute and overlay as follows:

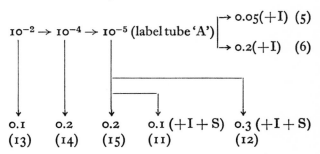

$10^{-2} \rightarrow 10^{-4} \rightarrow 10^{-5}$ (label tube 'A')

$\rightarrow$ 0.05(+I) (5)
$\rightarrow$ 0.2(+I)   (6)

0.1	0.2	0.2	0.1 (+I + S)	0.3 (+I + S)
(13)	(14)	(15)	(11)	(12)

7 Add 0.05 ml anti-T4 serum to adsorption tube.

10 Add 4 drops $CHCl_3$ to tube 'A'; shake gently for 10 sec and leave tube at room temperature.

13 Dilute and overlay from adsorption tube

10^{-5} —
$\rightarrow$ 0.2 (+I) . . . . . . (7)
$\rightarrow$ 0.4 (+I) . . . . . . (8)

18 Overlay from tube 'A' —
$\rightarrow$ 0.2 (+I) . . . . . . (9)
$\rightarrow$ 0.4 (+I) . . . . . . (10)

4. Incubate all plates overnight.

---

* All assays to be carried out by adding sample to a tube of soft agar at 46°. For phage assays on standard TNA plates, four drops of indicator bacteria must also be added (+I).

For phage assays on Strep TNA plates, 0.5 ml of indicator bacteria must be added, as the bacterial growth rate is slower in the presence of streptomycin. Also to adjust the streptomycin in concentration in the top agar, 0.3 ml of the 3% strep. solution must also be added. These two additions are designated (+ I + S).

Day following Part 1

1 Count the plates, and calculate the titres of the following:
> host bacteria (1,2)
> parental phage (3,4)
> unadsorbed phage (9,10), (11,12)
> infected cells (7,8)
> uninfected bacteria (13,14,15)
> infected cells plus unadsorbed phage (5,6).

2 Calculate the multiplicity of infection from the fraction of surviving bacteria, using the Poisson table.

3 Compare the three possible estimates which can be calculated from the results for the number of unadsorbed phage particles.

4 Calculate the multiplicity of infection from the bacterial concentration and the number of phage particles known to have been adsorbed. How does this value compare with one found in 2?

Experiment 14
One-step growth curve and the Doermann experiment

Background

It is known that on infection of bacterial cells with virulent phage particles, the phage DNA enters the bacterial cells and these cells then synthesize materials needed for phage production. After a certain time, mature phage particles form inside the infected cells. The production of mature phages proceeds at a constant rate until eventually the infected cells lyse, liberating up to 200 phage particles per cell. The time between infection and lysis is termed the *latent period*, which is characteristic for a particular phage and bacterial host strain. The first part of the latent period, during which no mature phage are present in the infected cell, is called the *eclipse period*.

The extent of the latent period and the intracellular development of phage can be measured by the 'one-step growth' experiment and the 'Doermann' experiment respectively.

One-step growth experiment (ELLIS & DELBRÜCK, 1939). In a one-step growth experiment, a culture of bacteria is synchronously infected with phage particles, and then samples are removed at different times after infection and immediately assayed for phage. On examining the plates the next day, it will be found that the first platings all give a constant number of plaques, corresponding to the number of infected cells present in the samples. The onset of lysis in the cells (which defines the extent of the latent period) is then heralded by a sudden increase in the number of plaques found from later platings. This number increases for a further time, sometimes called the *rise period*, until all the infected cells have lysed. At later times, a constant number of plaques is again found on the plates, corresponding to the total number of phages liberated by all the infected cells. The average burst size can then be calculated from the ratio of this final number to the number of infected cells originally present in the mixture.

Doermann experiment (DOERMANN 1952). Samples from a synchronously-infected culture are removed at intervals and the infected cells are artificially lysed, thus liberating any mature phage present at the time of the artificial lysis. In the present experiment, lysis is induced by a high concentration of streptomycin (see SYMONDS, 1957). After lysis, these samples are assayed for phage. In contrast to the one-step growth experiment, where the samples give a constant number of plaques up to the end of the latent period, in the Doermann experiment, the samples give no plaques until the end of the eclipse period, and then the plaque count increases continuously until lysis has occurred in all the infected cells. This experiment demonstrates the extent of the eclipse period and the rate of intracellular phage production in the infected cells.

References
ELLIS, E.L. & M.DELBRÜCK (1939) *J. Gen. Physiol.* **22**, 365.
DOERMANN, A.H. (1952) *J. Gen. Physiol.* **35**, 645.
SYMONDS, N.D. (1957) *Virology*, **3**, 485.

Intention

The experiment measures the kinetics of phage development as described above, using *E.coli* B and phage T4.

Requirements

Part 1   *Host Bacteria*—1 ml log. culture *E.coli* B (EMG 31) in phage-broth containing M/500 KCN.
Indicator Bacteria—10 ml o/n phage-broth culture of *E.coli* B/S (EMG 32).
0.5 ml T4 phage at 2×10^8 particles/ml.
1 ml streptomycin solution (3%).
0.1 ml anti-T4-phage serum (K = 20).
25 TNA plates.
100 ml soft agar (molten at 46°).
50 ml phage-broth.
25 ml buffer.
8 large tubes.
31 small tubes.

Method

Part 1   **1** Prepare 5 buffer dilution tubes (4×5 ml; 1×2.5 ml).
2 hr

Prepare 3 tubes phage-broth (2×10 ml; 1×9.5 ml). Place in 37° bath.

25 tubes of soft agar. Place in 46° bath. (Add 0.5 ml indicator bacteria to each tube before plating).

6 tubes containing 0.1 ml streptomycin labelled 3,10,15,20,25 and 31. Place in 37° bath.

2 Place small tube with 1 ml host bacteria (adsorption tube) in 37° waterbath and leave about 10 min.

Time (min)

0   Add 0.1 ml of T4 phage to host bacteria in adsorption tube.

8   Add 0.05 ml of antiserum to adsorption tube.

14   Dilute from adsorption tube into warm broth and plate (overlay) as follows:

$$\frac{0.1}{10} \to \frac{0.1}{10} \to \frac{0.5}{9.5} \text{ (Tube 'A')}$$

$$\downarrow \downarrow$$
$$0.2 \text{ ml}$$
Plates (1) & (2)

Keep tube 'A' at 37°.

Take the following samples and platings (in soft agar with indicator bacteria), *all directly from tube 'A'*:

17   Take 1 ml to streptomycin tube 3.

20   Plate 0.2 ml (3).

24   Take 1 ml to streptomycin tube 10.

26   Plate 0.2 ml (4).

29   Take 1 ml to streptomycin tube 15.

32   Plate 0.2 ml (5).

34   Take 1 ml to streptomycin tube 20.

35   Plate 0.2 ml (6).

38   Plate 0.1 ml (7).

39   Take 1 ml to streptomycin tube 25.

41   Plate 0.05 ml (8).

44   Plate 0.05 ml (9).

45   Take 1 ml to streptomycin tube 31.

Time (min)

59   Dilute and plate from tube 'A'

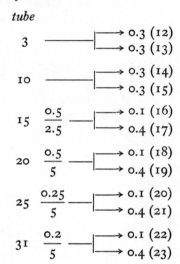

80   Dilute from streptomycin tubes and add the volumes indicated to soft agar tubes with indicator bacteria and overlay as follows:

3   Plate indicator bacteria without sample. Plates (24) and (25).

4   Incubate plates overnight.

Day following Part 1

Part 2   1   Count the plaques on all the plates.

2 hr   2   Plot the results of the one-step growth experiment and the Doermann experiment on both ordinary and semi-log paper (time on linear axis).

3   Estimate from the curves, the extents of the latent period, the eclipse period, the burst-size and the rate of production per cell of mature phage particles.

Experiment 15
Chemical mutagenesis with 5-bromouracil

Background

According to the model of Watson and Crick, the DNA molecule consists of two polynucleotide chains arranged in the form of a double helix. The backbone of these chains is a regular sequence of sugar and phosphate groups. To each sugar molecule is attached one of the four nitrogenous bases, adenine, guanine, thymine, or cytosine. The double helix is held together by hydrogen bonds between the bases attached to each chain. Only the specific base-pairs adenine-thymine and guanine-cytosine can form stable hydrogen bonds, but there is no structural limitation on the order in which the base-pairs follow one another along the double chain. For this reason it is considered that the 'information' contained in genes (which control the formation of specific proteins) is 'coded' by the sequence in which the base-pairs occur along the double helix. If by any means one base-pair is changed to another, the sequence is altered and such a change can lead to a mutation. During replication these changes occur spontaneously at a low rate; however, it is possible to increase this spontaneous rate considerably by the use of mutagens. Certain 'base-analogues' are known which are highly mutagenic; if present during replication, these chemical compounds are sufficiently similar in structure to the normal bases to be incorporated into DNA. However, they are sufficiently different so as to increase the probability of errors in base-pairing during subsequent replication, and thus increase the mutation rate. An example of such a mutagen is 5-bromouracil, which differs from thymine only in the substitution of a bromine atom for a methyl group.

References
FREESE E. (1959) *J. mol. Biol.* **1**, 87.
LITMAN R. & A.PARDEE (1956) *Nature,* **178**, 529.

Intention

In the present experiment, bacteria are grown in a medium which specifically inhibits thymine synthesis. In order for growth to occur, the bacteria must incorporate 5-bromouracil, which is present in the medium, into their DNA. After some generations of bacterial growth, these bacteria are infected at a low multiplicity with wild-type T4 phage, and lysis is allowed to occur. In the phage progeny a large number of phage mutants will be found which can be recognized by their altered plaque type.

Requirements

Part 1   *Host Bacteria*—1 ml of an o/n culture of *E.coli* B (EMG 31) grown in M9 medium (Appendix A13).
Indicator Bacteria—1 ml of an o/n culture of *E.coli* B grown in phage-broth.

0.5 ml 'wild-type' T4 phage at a concentration of 10^9 particles/ml.

5 ml M9 medium containing the following supplements (in μg/ml): L-tryptophan (10), sulphanilamide (1000), casamino acids (vitamin-free) (1000), xanthine (25), 5-bromouracil (50), uracil (2.5).

Chloroform
7 TNA plates
25 ml soft agar (molten at 46°)
100 ml buffer
17 large tubes
8 small tubes
1 large aeration tube

Method

Part 1   1 Prepare: 7 × 10 ml buffer tubes
(6 hr—with   8 tubes molten soft agar (place in 46° bath)
intervals)   Label TNA plates 1–7

2 Inoculate the 5 ml of supplemented M9 medium with 0.2 ml of the o/n culture of M9-grown host bacteria. Place tube in 37° bath and incubate for 30 min without aeration, and then aerate for a further 2 hr. (Immediate bubbling of cells grown overnight in synthetic medium can kill a large proportion.)

3 Add 0.05 ml of the phage, and continue aeration for a further 3 hr.

4 Add 4 drops of CHCl₃ to the tube, shake gently for 10 sec, and leave tube for 15 min at room temperature.

5 Assay as follows (phage-broth culture as indicator):

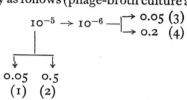

6 Assay also the parental phage stock:

$$10^{-6} \longrightarrow \begin{array}{l} \rightarrow 0.3 \; (5) \\ \rightarrow 0.3 \; (6) \\ \rightarrow 0.3 \; (7) \end{array}$$

7 Incubate the plates overnight.

Day following Part 1

Part 2
½ hr

1 Count the total number of plaques on each plate and note the number of plaques with an altered morphology.

2 Compare the fraction of plaque-type mutants present in the parent phage stock (5–7) with that after mutagenesis with 5-bromouracil (1–4).

Experiment 16
Phage crosses
(Can be performed concurrently with Experiments 17 and 18.)

Background

Several types of mutants having distinct phenotypic properties have been isolated in the phages T2 and T4. The mutant types used in these following experiments are:

(a) *'Host-range' mutants of phage T2*. *E.coli* B is sensitive to phage T2, but bacterial mutant strains, the one used in this experiment called B/2, can be isolated which are resistant to phage T2. It is possible to isolate from the 'wild-type' T2 strain, mutants which can infect and lyse the strain B/2. Such mutants have a more extensive host-range than T2 wild-type, and are designated by the term T2*h*.

(b) *'Rapid-lysis' mutants of phages T2 and T4*. The plaques produced by wild-type T2 (and T4) have a clear centre surrounded by a turbid halo. Mutants have been isolated which produce larger and uniformly clear plaques. These are called rapid-lysis or *r* mutants. Independent isolates of these *r* mutants are genetically distinct. These *r* mutants map in three distinct regions of the phage linkage group (chromosome) and are thereby classified as *rI*, *rII* and *rIII* mutants. Mutants of the *rII* group can be further distinguished from other *r* mutants by the property that they are unable to produce plaques on a λ-lysogenic strain of *E.coli* K12, here called *K(λ)*.

In a phage cross, sensitive bacteria are multiply infected with phage mutants which are genetically distinct. The phage progeny arising from these infected bacteria are formed of phage particles of the parental types, and also of recombinant phage particles possessing characters derived from each of the parents. In crosses where only two genetic markers are used, the percentage of recombinants in the progeny serves as an index of the proximity of the markers on the phage chromosome.

References
BENZER, S. (1955) *Proc. Natl. Acad. Sci., Wash.*, **41**, 344.
HERSHEY, A.D. & R.ROTMAN (1949) *Genetics* **34**, 44.

Intention

Two crosses will be performed in this experiment:

(a) *T2hrI × T2 'wild'*. The four possible genotypes arising in this cross can be distinguished phenotypically by plating with a 'mixed-indicator' which is a mixture of cultures of the bacterial strains *E.coli* B and *E.coli* B/2. A phage with the host-range mutation (T2*h*) can lyse both B and B/2, and its plaques are thus clear. However, the wild-type phage (T2*h*+) can lyse only the B cells in the mixed-indicator layer. Thus the B/2 cells grow within a zone of lysis of B and produce a 'turbid' plaque. The plaque types that are seen are therefore as follows:

	Genotype		Plaque type
Parents	*h*	*rI*	clear, large
	+	+	turbid, small
Recombinants	+	*rI*	turbid, large
	h	+	clear, small

(b) *T4rII(147) × T4rII(271)*. This cross is between two independently-isolated *rII* mutants, neither of which can form plaques on K(λ). In this cross, *E.coli* B is multiply-infected with both phages. Of the subsequent progeny, as can be seen below, only the wild-type recombinant can be distinguished phenotypically from the parent phage. The number of such recombinants is easily determined by assaying the progeny directly on K(λ).

	Genotype rII		Plaque-type on E.coli B	K(λ)
Parents	*147*	+	*r* (large)	—*
	+	*271*	*r* (large)	—*
Recombinants	*147*	*271*	*r* (large)	—*
	+	+	*r*+ (small)	*r*+ (small)

In addition to strains B (EMG31) and B/S (EMG32) used in previous experiments, the *E.coli* B strain resistant to phage T2, termed B/2 (EMG33) and a wild-type lysogenic *E.coli* K12 strain, termed K(λ) (EMG2) are required as overnight phage-broth cultures.

* No plaques formed.

Requirements

Host Bacteria—2 × 0.5 ml of a log. culture of *E.coli* B (3 × 10^8 cells/ml) in phage-broth containing M/250 KCN, made by centrifuging a log. culture of 10^8 cells/ml and resuspending in $\frac{1}{3}$ vol of fresh, warm phage-broth + KCN.

Indicator Bacteria—5 ml of overnight cultures of *E. coli* B, *E.coli* B/S, *E.coli* B/2 and *E.coli* K(λ) in phage-broth. Take 2 ml B and mix with 1 ml B/2. This is the 'mixed indicator'—label this indicator *M*.

Phage. A mixture of the two parental phages is prepared for each cross containing 2 × 10^9 particles per ml of each parental type

    Cross *A*—T2*hrI* × T2 'wild'
    Cross *B*—T4*rII(147)* × T4*rII(271)*.

16 TNA plates.
2 Strep TNA plates (see footnote, p.72).
2 ml (3%) streptomycin solution.
50 ml phage-broth
200 ml buffer.
100 ml soft agar (molten at 46°).
18 large tubes.
18 small tubes.

Method

Part 1
2 hr

1 Prepare: 14 dilution tubes (8 × 10 ml; 6 × 9 ml).
    4 × 10 ml broth tubes. Place in 37° bath.
    18 tubes molten soft agar. Add 0.3 ml streptomycin solution to 2 of these tubes. Place in 46° bath.

2 Label TNA plates 1–16; Strep TNA plates 17 & 18.

3 Put the two tubes containing 0.5 ml host bacteria in 37° waterbath and label 'A' and 'B'. Leave for about 10 min.

4 During this time, assay the parental phage mixtures by diluting and plating *viz*.

Cross A: $10^{-7} \to 2 \times 0.4$ ml with M
Plates (1 & 2)
Cross B: $10^{-4} \to 0.1$ ml with $K(\lambda)$ (3)
↓
$10^{-7} \to 0.4$ ml with B (4)

5 Then proceed as follows:

Time (min)

0 Add 0.5 ml of phage mixture A to tube 'A'.

3 Add 0.5 ml of phage mixture B to tube 'B'.

8 Dilute 10^{-4} from tube 'A' into warm broth; label final dilution tube 'A1' and leave at 37°.

9 Dilute 10^{-1} from tube 'A1'
and plate $\longrightarrow$ 0.05 ml with B (5)
$\to$ 0.2 ml with B (6)
$\to$ 0.2 ml with B/S   (17)

11 Dilute 10^{-4} from tube 'B' into warm broth; label final dilution tube 'B1' and leave at 37°.

12 Dilute 10^{-1} from tube 'B1'
and plate $\longrightarrow$ 0.05 ml with B (7)
$\to$ 0.2 ml with B (8)
$\to$ 0.2 ml with B/S (18)

90 Dilute from tube 'A1'
$10^{-2} \longrightarrow$ plate 0.1 ml with M (9)
↓ $\to$ plate 0.4 ml with M (10)
$10^{-3} \longrightarrow$ plate 0.1 ml with M (11)
$\to$ plate 0.4 ml with M (12)

93 Dilute from tube 'B1'
$10^{-1} \longrightarrow$ plate 0.1 ml with $K(\lambda)$ (13)
↓ $\to$ plate 0.2 ml with $K(\lambda)$ (14)
$10^{-3} \longrightarrow$ plate 0.1 ml with B (15)
$\to$ plate 0.2 ml with B (16)

6 Incubate all plates overnight.

85

Day following Part 1

Part 2   *Cross A—T2hrI × T2 wild*

1 hr   **1** Calculate the titre of both phage types in the parental mixture (1,2).

2 Observe the distinct plaque types in plates (5) and (6). What is the origin of these plaques?

3 Score all four plaque-types observable in the progeny of the cross (9,10,11,12). Calculate the fraction of recombinants in the progeny.

Cross B—T4rII(147) × T4rII(271)

1 Calculate the titre of the phage in the parental mixture (4). How could the number of each parental type in the parental mixture be found experimentally? What is the purpose of the plating (3)?

2 Calculate the fraction of wild-type recombinants in progeny of the cross (13,14,15,16).

3 Calculate the multiplicity of infection and the average burst size in the cross.

Experiment 17
Spot tests with *rII* mutants of T4 phage
(Can be performed concurrently with Experiments 16 and 18.)

Intention

BENZER (1957) has shown that the *rII* region of the T4 chromosome can be divided into two parts, called the *A* and *B* cistrons. Phages having a mutation in either cistron are unable to produce plaques on plates seeded with *E.coli* $K(\lambda)$. However, if cells of $K(\lambda)$ are infected with *both* an *rIIA and* an *rIIB* mutant, then phage production does occur in these cells as a result of complementation. This can be simply demonstrated as a spot test by plating 10^8 particles of an *rIIA* mutant with $K(\lambda)$ and adding to the plate separate drops containing 10^6 particles either of an *rIIA* or an *rIIB* mutant. In the spot where both *rIIA* and *rIIB* phage are present, extensive lysis occurs, but in the other spot there is no lysis. This test forms the basis of a quick method for locating any newly-isolated *rII* mutants in either the *A* or *B* cistron.

Reference
BENZER S. (1958) In *Chemical Basis of Heredity*, Eds. McElroy W.D. and B.Glass, p.70. Johns Hopkins Press: Baltimore.

Requirements

Part 1   *Indicator Bacteria*—2 ml of o/n cultures in phage broth of *E.coli* B (EMG31) and *E.coli* K(λ)(EMG2).

Phages:
(i) 0.1 ml T4*rIIA164* at 10^9pfu/ml
    0.1 ml T4*rIIB196* at 10^9pfu/ml
    These are representative *rII* mutations in the *A* and *B* cistrons
(ii) 0.1 ml T4 wild type at 10^7 particles/ml.
    0.1 ml T4*rIIA147* at 10^7 particles/ml.
    0.1 ml T4*rIIB114* at 10^7 particles/ml.
    0.1 ml T4*rIIABH23* (a deletion across the *rIIA*

and *rIIB* cistrons) at 10^7 particles/ml*
4 TNA plates.
20 ml soft agar (molten at 46°).
4 small tubes.

Method

Part 1
½ hr

1 Prepare 4 tubes molten soft agar. Place in 46° bath.

2 Label plates 1–4 and mark the back into four quadrants.

3 Overlay the plates with the following indicator bacteria and phage:
   (1) B
   (2) K(λ)
   (3) K(λ) + 0.1 ml *rIIA164*
   (4) K(λ) + 0.1 ml *rIIB196*

4 Leave plates on bench for 15 min for overlay to set.

5 With a 0.1 ml pipette, spot one drop of each of the four phage preparations provided at 10^7 particles/ml on each plate, one in each quadrant.

6 Allow spots to soak in.

7 Incubate plates overnight.

Day following Part 1

Part 2
15 min

From the pattern of phage lysis, what can be said about the genetic structure of the phages added as spots?

* To add interest to the experiment, these phages should be labelled in an arbitrary way by the instructor and presented to the student as four unknowns.

Experiment 18
Spot tests with conditional-lethal phage mutants
Can be carried out in the same period as Expts. 16 and 17

Intention

Normally the wild-type phage T4 plates equally well either on *E.coli* B or on a derivative strain of *E.coli* K12 designated CR63. However, a class of phage mutants called '*amber*' (*am*) (which may be defective in any cistron in phage T4) has been isolated by EPSTEIN, which have lost their ability to plate on B, but retain their ability to plate with high efficiency on CR63. For these *amber* mutants, CR63 is termed a 'permissive' strain and strain B is 'non-permissive'.

Phage T4 normally plates equally well both at 25° and 42°. Again mutants can be found in most cistrons which still plate at the low temperature, but have lost the ability to plate at the higher one. These *temperature-sensitive* (*ts*) mutants respond similarly on both strain B and CR63. Both these types of mutants are termed *conditional lethal*, since they are lethal only under certain conditions of growth.

Complementation tests, similar to that described above for the *rII* mutants, can be used to determine whether two conditional-lethal mutants of either *am* or *ts* type are in the same, or in different cistrons.

Reference
EPSTEIN *et al.* (1963) *Cold Spr. Harb. Symp. Quant. Biol.*, **28**, 375.

Requirements

Phage
(i) 0.2 ml of an *amber* mutant of T4 (*amA*) in gene 56 at 10^9 particles/ml.
(ii) 0.2 ml of each of four T4 conditional-lethal mutants each at 10^7 particles/ml.*†
(iii) 0.2 ml wild-type T4 phage at 10^7 particles/ml.†

---

* Suitable phages for use would be two *am* mutants (one in gene 56 and the other in another gene e.g. gene 1) and two *ts* mutants (one in gene 56 and the other in another e.g. gene 19).

† These phage preparations should be labelled in an arbitrary manner by the instructor.

Indicator bacteria
2 ml o/n cultures of *E.coli* B (EMG31) and *E.coli* CR63 (EMG13) in phage-broth.
6 TNA plates.
20 ml soft agar (molten at 46°).
6 small tubes.

Method

Part 1
½ hr

1 Prepare 6 tubes molten soft agar. Place in 46° bath.

2 Label TNA plates 1–6 and mark the backs into five segments.

3 Overlay the plates with the following indicator bacteria and phage:
   (1) and (2) CR63
   (3) and (4) B
   (5) and (6) B + 0.1 ml T4 *amA*.

4 Leave the plates on the bench for 15 min for overlays to set.

5 With a 0.1 ml pipette, spot one drop of each of the unknown five phage preparations provided at 10^7 particles/ml on each plate, one spot per segment.

6 Allow spots to soak in.

7 Incubate plates (1),(3),(5), overnight at 25°, and plates (2),(4), and (6) overnight at 42°.

Day following Part 1.

Part 2
15 min

From the pattern of phage lysis, what can be said about the genetic structure of the phages added as spots?

Experiments 19, 20 & 21
Temperate phage and lysogeny

Background

The course of infection following the adsorption of a temperate phage particle to a sensitive bacterial cell may follow one of two alternative paths (see Fig.5).

1. The *vegetative* (productive) response, such as usually follows adsorption of a virulent phage particle (e.g. T phage), resulting in the lysis of the cell and the liberation of a burst of phage particles.

2. The *lysogenic* (reductive) response, resulting after a variable number of bacterial divisions in the establishment of a state of genetic symbiosis, in which the phage genetic material (prophage) is stabilized and regulated in a latent state in the bacterial cell. In some cases, such as with phage λ in *E.coli* K12, the prophage is known to be inserted into the continuity of the bacterial chromosome and to replicate in synchrony with it. Bacteria which harbour prophages are termed 'lysogenic' and the majority of the cells within such a bacterial culture maintain the phage in the regulated and controlled prophage state. Occasionally, however, this stable relationship breaks down, whereupon the vegetative phage cycle ensues and free phage particles are liberated. A certain number of free phage particles are therefore always likely to be present in any culture of lysogenic bacteria. An additional feature shown by lysogenic strains is that those cells in which prophage is stabilized are 'immune' to lysis by the same (and most related) phages. In general, a related phage particle can adsorb to an immune cell and inject its DNA, but its multiplication is repressed. In some instances, the genetic material of such *superinfecting* particles can either replace the existing prophage or form a doubly-lysogenic bacterium. In the case of some phages (e.g. λ), both *immunity*, and the establishment and maintenance of lysogeny, appear to be controlled by the presence of specific cytoplasmic *repressor* molecules, preventing synthesis of precursors for vegetative phage development. Phage particles having a mutation in the repressor gene cannot establish lysogeny, and therefore yield *clear* instead of *turbid* plaques.

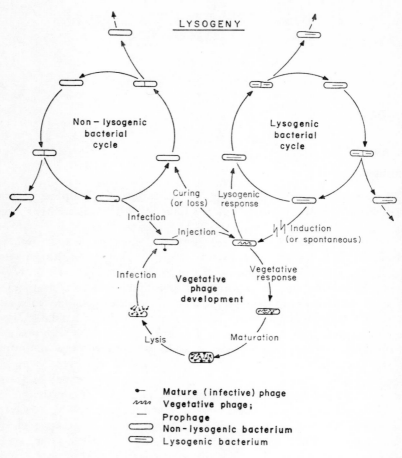

Fig.5 Lysogeny

The state of immunity differs in this way from phage *resistance*. This latter state is due in the case of temperate phages, as with virulent phages, to a mutation giving rise to a surface change in the bacterial cell wall so that a particular phage is no longer adsorbed.

Reference

STENT G.S. (1963) Molecular Biology of Bacterial Viruses. W.H.Freeman: San Francisco & London.

Experiment 19
Isolation of lysogenic bacteria and of clear-plaque mutants of a temperate phage

Intention

The purpose of this experiment is to assay a stock of the temperate phage P22 on the host bacterial strain, *Salmonella typhimurium* LT2; to isolate from it 'clear-plaque' (i.e. non-lysogenizing) mutants and to infect the sensitive host bacterium so as to produce a lysogenic strain in which the phage is perpetuated in the prophage state.

Requirements

Part 1   *Bacteria*—0.5 ml of an o/n broth culture of strain EMG36 (*S.typhimurium* LT2, sensitive to P22 phage).
           Phage—0.1 ml phage P22 (wild) at 2×10^9 plaque-forming units (pfu)/ml.*
           2 nutrient agar (NA) plates.
           10 ml soft agar (molten at 46°).
           50 ml buffer.
           3 large tubes.
           2 small tubes.

Part 2   1 ml o/n broth culture strain EMG36.
           9 NA plates.
           25 ml soft agar (molten at 46°).
           100 ml buffer.
           9 large tubes.
           9 small tubes.

* See p. 8 for preparation of P22 phage.

Part 3   2 ml log. broth culture strain EMG36.
1 ml o/n broth culture strain EMG36.
9 NA plates.
20 ml soft agar (molten at 46°).
150 ml buffer.
Chloroform.
3 small aeration tubes (see p.11).
12 large tubes.
6 small tubes.

Part 4   0.5 ml o/n broth culture strain EMG36.
0.1 ml P22 phage (2×10^9 pfu/ml).
1 NA plate.
6 small tubes.
5 ml buffer.

Part 5   2 NA plates.

Method

Part 1   **1** Prepare 3 dilution tubes (3×10 ml).
15 min   Prepare 2 soft agar tubes. Place in 46° bath.

2 Dilute the P22 phage preparation by 10^{-6} and plate 0.1 ml together with 0.1 ml EMG36 culture (standard assay as for virulent phage) in a soft agar overlay on each of two NA plates. Plates (1) & (2).

3 Incubate plates overnight.

Day following Part 1

Part 2   **1** Prepare 9 dilution tubes (6×10 ml; 3×9 ml)
$\frac{1}{2}$ hr   3 small tubes of $\frac{1}{2}$ ml buffer
6 soft agar tubes. Place in 46° bath.

2 Examine plates (1) & (2). Most of the plaques will have turbid centres, characteristic of the P22 (wild-type) phage. Examine the plates for clear plaques. Stab one clear plaque with a straight sterile wire and rinse in $\frac{1}{2}$ ml buffer. Repeat for two other clear plaques. Dilute each of these inoculated buffer solutions 10^{-3} and 10^{-5} and plate 0.1 ml from each in soft agar with 0.1 ml EMG36 culture on a NA plate. Plates (3) to (8).

2 Touch the bacterial growth within the centre of one of the turbid plaques with a small loop and streak over a NA plate to produce single bacterial colonies. Repeat for two other turbid plaques. Plates (9) to (11).

3 Finally, count the total number of turbid plaques on plates (1) and (2). Calculate the phage titre in the preparation supplied in Part 1.

4 Incubate plates (3) to (11) overnight.

Day following Part 2.

Part 3
(2 periods
of ½ hr,
separated
by 5 hr)

1 Prepare 3 aeration tubes containing ½ ml log. culture of EMG36. Place in 37° bath and aerate gently. Prepare 12 dilution tubes (10 ml). Prepare 6 soft agar tubes. Place in 46° bath.

2 From each pair of the plates (3) to (8) showing well-isolated clear plaques, stab one plaque into ½ ml of aerated log. culture of EMG36 and continue aeration for 5 hr at 37°. Then add 1 drop chloroform to each tube and incubate without aeration for ½ hr. Dilute each 10^{-6} and 10^{-8} and plate 0.1 ml from each dilution in soft agar on a NA plate with 0.1 ml o/n culture of EMG36. Plates (12) to (17). Retain chloroformed preparations for use as unknown P22*c* mutants in Experiment 22.

3 From plates (9) to (11) streaked with bacteria from the turbid plaques (Part 2) select *one* showing well-isolated colonies. Restreak three colonies on three further NA plates for single colonies—'purification plates' (18) to (20).

4 Incubate plates (12) to (20) overnight.

Day following Part 3

<table>
<tr><td>

Part 4

½ hr
</td><td>

1 Prepare 6 tubes ½ ml buffer.

2 Examine plates (12) to (17). One of each pair should show a homogeneous population of clear plaques.* Note any differences in morphology between plaques of different origins. Count the numbers of plaques on each plate and thus assay the titre in each of the chloroformed preparations.

3 Mark the back of the NA plate provided, to form eight segments. From each of the three purification plates (18) to (20), select two well-separated colonies and inoculate each into ½ ml buffer to produce a suspension of $c.10^8$ cells/ml. With a 0.1 ml pipette, place a drop from each tube on a separate segment of the plate. On each of the two remaining segments, spot an inoculum from the o/n broth culture provided. Allow drops to soak in. Then with a sterile loop, spot 1 drop of the phage provided in the centre of each inoculated segment.

4 Incubate overnight. Plate (21).
</td></tr>
</table>

Day following Part 4

<table>
<tr><td>

Part 5

10 min
</td><td>

1 Examine plate (21). The growth of the control strain EMG36 should show an area of lysis by the added phage. The other areas will show similar lysis if the inoculum was from a purification plate spread with bacteria that had remained phage-sensitive. Most areas should in fact show no inhibition and the corresponding purification plates (18) to (20) therefore contain lysogenic bacteria which are immune to the phage.

2 Streak from the peripheral growth on Plate 21 from two areas which do *not* show lysis by P22 phage to the NA plates provided. Plates (22) & (23).
</td></tr>
</table>

* If the population is heterogeneous in plaque morphology, Part 3 (2) should be repeated.

3 Incubate plates overnight and retain to test for presence of phage released from these lysogenic bacteria as in Experiment 20.

Experiment 20
Immunity and phage production by lysogenic bacteria

Intention

This experiment is designed to show the presence of free phage particles in a culture of a lysogenic strain of bacteria, and to show that, in contrast to the corresponding sensitive strain, it is insensitive (immune) to the action of the phage.

Requirements

Part 1	*Bacteria*
	1 ml o/n broth culture strain EMG37 (*S.typhimurium* LT2, sensitive to P22 phage, *str-r*).
	1 ml o/n broth culture strain EMG38 (*S.typhimurium* LT2, lysogenic for P22 phage, *str-s*).
	1 ml o/n broth cultures from each of two newly-isolated lysogenic derivatives of strain EMG36 (Plates 22, and 23, Expt.19).
	Phage—0.5 ml P22 (wild) phage suspension at 10^9 pfu/ml.
	1 NA plate.
	1 NA + SM plate (200 μg/ml streptomycin).
	5 ml soft agar (molten at 46°).
	1 small tube.

Method

Part 1 $\frac{1}{2}$ hr	**1** Prepare 1 soft agar tube. Place in 46° bath. Mark the backs of both plates into quadrants.
	2 Using a 0.1 ml pipette, spot 1 drop of the four broth cultures each to a quadrant of the NA plate. Allow to soak in (15 min). Then spot a drop of phage with a sterile loop onto each area of bacterial inoculum. Allow to soak in.

98

3 Add 0.1 ml of strain EMG37 to the soft agar tube and overlay the NA + SM plate. Allow 15 min for overlay to set. Spot a drop of each of the four bacterial cultures each on a separate quadrant of the plate and a spot of P22 phage in the centre of the plate. Allow drops to soak in.

4 Incubate both plates overnight.

Day following Part 1

Part 2   1 On the NA plate, strain EMG37 should show an
15 min   area of lysis by the added phage, whereas strain
             EMG38 should not.

2 On the NA + SM plate, the spot of the lysogenic EMG38 culture should show either an area of lysis or separated phage plaques on the lawn of EMG37, due to the presence of free phage particles arising from spontaneous lysis.

3 Do the unknown strains from Expt.19 behave as lysogenic under *both* these tests?

4 Compare the results with Experiment 19 (Part 5/1).

Experiment 21
Experiments with λ phages and λ lysogenic bacteria of *E.coli* K12

Intention

The experiments set out to show phage sensitivity, immunity and lysogeny as in the previous experiments. In addition, they show the effect of bacterial resistance, defective lysogeny (where the prophage although giving rise to immunity, cannot give rise to active particles) and also the effect of phage mutations, one of which prevents the prophage state being developed and another in which the infecting phage does not respond to the normal immunity system.

The following *E.coli* K12 bacterial strains will be required as o/n broth cultures for this experiment.
a. EMG21. This strain is lysogenic for λ and adsorbs λ, i.e. $(\lambda)^{+}\lambda\text{-}s$
b. EMG10. This strain (which is *str-r*) is non-lysogenic for λ and adsorbs λ i.e. $(\lambda)^{-}\lambda\text{-}s$.
c. EMG14. This strain is non-lysogenic for λ but does not adsorb λ i.e. $(\lambda)^{-}\lambda\text{-}r$.
d. EMG15. This strain is lysogenic for a defective λ phage and adsorbs λ i.e. $(\lambda d)\lambda\text{-}s$.

In addition, lysates of the following three λ phages at 10^{10} pfu/ml are required:

λ^{+}, the wild-type λ

λc, a 'clear-plaque' mutant and

λv, a virulent mutant which lyses λ-lysogenic cells.

See p. 8 for their preparation.

Requirements

Part 1	1 ml o/n broth culture strain EMG21.
	1 ml o/n broth culture strain EMG10.
	1 ml o/n broth culture strain EMG14.
	1 ml o/n broth culture strain EMG15.
	0.1 ml 10^{10} pfu/ml λ^{+} phage.

0.1 ml 10^{10} pfu/ml λc phage.
0.1 ml 10^{10} pfu/ml λv phage.
3 NA plates.
2 NA + SM plates.
20 ml soft agar (molten at 46°).
5 small tubes.

Method

Part 1
½ hr

1 Prepare 5 soft agar tubes. Place in 46° bath.
Mark the back of each plate into quadrants.

2 Overlay one NA plate with soft agar   Plates
containing 0.1 ml EMG21   (1)
Overlay one NA plate with soft agar
containing 0.1 ml EMG14   (2)
Overlay one NA plate with soft agar
containing 0.1 ml EMG15   (3)
Overlay two NA + SM plates with
soft agar containing 0.1 ml EMG10   (4) & (5)
Allow 15 min for overlays to set.

3 On the 3 NA plates (1) to (3) and one of the
NA + SM plates (4), spot one drop of each of the
three phage suspensions, each on a separate quadrant, using a 0.1 ml pipette.

4 On the remaining NA + SM plate (5), spot one
drop of each bacterial culture, one to each quadrant. Allow drops to soak in (15 min).

6 Incubate plates overnight.

Day following Part 1

Part 2
½ hr

1 Note the zones of lysis on the plates.

2 Of the phages spotted on plates (1) to (4), λ^+
should produce *turbid* plaques on EMG10 only,
λc should produce *clear* plaques on EMG10 only,
λv should produce *clear* plaques on EMG21, 10
and 15 only.

3 Of the bacterial cultures spotted on plate (5), only
EMG21 should produce lysis or plaques (turbid,
since due to λ) on the EMG10 lawn.

Experiment 22
Complementation between clear-plaque mutants of temperate phage P22 in *Salmonella typhimurium*

Background

On examining a large number of plaques formed by a temperate phage, such as P22, clear plaques are usually found at a frequency of about 1 in 10^3 (see Expt.19). If these plaques are picked, they breed true and are representative of mutants which have lost the ability to lysogenize, but maintain the capacity to lyse. Several independent, functional steps are necessary to establish lysogeny and this can be demonstrated by the fact that clear-plaque mutants can be sub-divided into several complementation groups.

The complementation test for lysogeny depends on the ability of certain pairs of different clear-plaque phage mutants, when mixedly infecting the same cell, to cooperate in assisting *one* of the mutants to establish the prophage state. The resultant cell is thus lysogenic for a phage which on liberation maintains its clear-plaque (non-lysogenic) character. By this test, clear-plaque mutants of P22 fall into three groups, in which any phage of one group can cooperate with any phage of the other two groups to establish lysogeny.

References
KAISER A.D. (1957) *Virology* **3**, 42.
LEVINE M. (1957) *Virology* **3**, 22.

Intention

The experiment is a spot test involving P22 phage mutants from each of the groups *c1* and *c2*, together with the wild-type (c^+) as a control and two unknown clear-plaque mutants. Each of the phages is plated in soft agar together with the indicator bacterium *Salmonella typhimurium* LT2; the other phages are then spotted on the agar layer before incubation. The plates then show *confluent* phage lysis, *except* at those areas where the phages cooperate to produce a turbid area of bacterial growth. Cells in this area can be shown to be lysogenic for *one* of the two phages concerned.

As a preliminary to the experiment, suspensions of the two clear-plaque mutant phages of P22, P22(*c1*) and P22(*c2*) are required, together with suspensions of the wild-type P22*c*⁺ phage (prepared as detailed on p.8) and the two chloroformed preparations of clear-plaque mutants obtained in Experiment 19 (Part 3/2).

Requirements

1 ml o/n broth culture, strain EMG36.
1 ml P22*c1* phage at 2×10^{10} pfu/ml.
1 ml P22*c2* phage at 2×10^{10} pfu/ml.
1 ml P22*c*⁺ phage at 2×10^{10} pfu/ml.
1 ml of each of the two preparations of P22 unknown clear-plaque mutants at about 2×10^{10} pfu/ml (from Expt.19).
7 NA plates.
20 ml soft agar (molten at 46°).
50 ml buffer.
4 large tubes.
7 small tubes.

Method

Part 1
1 hr

1 Prepare 4 dilution tubes (3×10 ml; 1×9 ml). 7 soft agar tubes. Place in 46° bath.

2 Dilute *either c1* or *c2* phage preparation (to be detailed by instructor) by 10^{-7} and plate 0.05 ml in soft agar with 0.1 ml strain EMG36 on each of two NA plates [P22*c* phage assay, Plates (1) & (2)].

3 Mark the back of the 5 remaining plates to divide into quadrants.
Add 0.1 ml of the 5 *undiluted* phage suspensions each to a separate soft agar tube with 0.1 ml of strain EMG36. Overlay each over a NA plate. Plates (3) to (7).
Allow overlays to set (15 min).

4 With a 0.1 ml pipette, place a spot of each of the same undiluted phage suspensions, one to each quadrant on each of the plates (3) to (7), omitting the phage previously incorporated in the overlay. Allow drops to soak in (15 min).

5 Incubate plates overnight.

Day following Part 1

Part 2
½ hr

1 Examine assay plates (1) and (2) and calculate titre of phage. Note morphology of each of the clear plaque types.

2 Examine complementation plates (3) to (7). Note that these show very little overall growth (due to confluent lysis of indicator bacteria with high concentrations of *plating* phage). However, where spots of phage were placed, these show a zone of enhanced bacterial growth when this second phage is either c^+ or a mutant of a different complementation group to the plated phage (*e.g. c1* spotted on *c2*)*.

3 To which complementation groups do the unknown clear-plaque mutants isolated in Expt.19 belong?

* If bacteria are isolated from the area of enhanced growth, these will be found to be immune to P22 phage and lysogenic for one of the two phages present in the area. If the wild c^+ phage was one of these phages, this phage would always establish lysogeny. If the two mutants *c1* and *c2* were involved, the phage established in lysogeny would always be *c2*.

Experiment 23
Host-controlled modification (HCM) with phages λ and P1 in *Escherichia coli* K12

Background

When only a small fraction of phage particles grown on one strain of bacteria succeed in growing on a second strain, there may be two reasons for the failure:

1. the second host is either resistant or immune, and the few phage particles that produce successful infections are *mutants* with an extended host-range, or a lack of response to the phage-immunity system (e.g. λ*v* mutants), or
2. the second host has a different system of 'host-controlled modification' (HCM) and the few successful particles are those which have escaped a 'restriction' which is levelled against the foreign DNA.

In both cases the progeny phage are fully infectious for the second host. These two possibilities can easily be distinguished. A mutant is genetically stable and retains its capacity to grow in the second host even after a cycle of growth in the first strain. The host-controlled change is not genetically stable and is lost after one cycle of growth in the first strain.

Intention

The experiment to be performed concerns a system of HCM which is controlled by the prophage P1. Phage λ.K (that is λ grown in a strain of *E.coli* K12 which is non-lysogenic for λ, termed K) will plate on strains of *E.coli* K12, also non-lysogenic for λ but lysogenic for P1, termed K(P1), with an efficiency of only 10^{-4} as compared with its plating ability on K (the original *E.coli* K12 strain). That is, there are 10^4 times more plaques on K as on K(P1). The progeny phage in the few plaques on K(P1) now plate with equal efficiency on both K and K(P1) bacteria. In order to test whether this change in property of the phage is due to mutation or to HCM, the λ.K(P1) phages are now grown in K once again. It is found that their behaviour reverts to that of the initial λ.K phage, showing that these differences in behaviour observed in λ are brought about by HCM.

Efficiency of plating on strains of *E.coli*

Phage	E. Coli	
	K	K(P1)
λ.K	1	10^{-4}
λ.K(P1)	1	1
λ.K(P1)—after regrowth in K	1	10^{-4}

The two strains K and K(P1) are strains EMG10 and EMG16 respectively (*both being C600 strains*). Phage λ is obtained by the confluent lysis method on EMG10 (Introduction, p. 8). This is, of course, λ.K phage.

References
ARBER W. & D.DUSSOIX (1962) *J. Mol. Biol.* **5**, 18.
ARBER W. (1965) *Ann. Rev. Microbiol.* **19**, 365.

Requirements

Part 1   1 ml o/n broth cultures of strains K and K(P1).
0.5 ml phage λ.K at 10^7 pfu/ml.
4 nutrient agar (NA) plates.
15 ml soft agar (molten at 46°).
50 ml buffer.
2 large tubes.
4 small tubes.

Part 2   1 ml o/n broth cultures of strains K and K(P1).
8 NA plates.
25 ml soft agar (molten at 46°).
50 ml buffer.
4 large tubes.
12 small tubes.
4 sterile toothpicks.

Part 3   1 ml o/n broth cultures of K and K(P1).
16 NA plates.
50 ml soft agar (molten at 46°).
100 ml buffer.
8 large tubes.
24 small tubes.
8 sterile toothpicks.

Method

<table>
<tr><td>Part 1
15 min</td><td>

1 Prepare 2 dilution tubes (2×10 ml).
4 soft agar tubes. Place in $46°$ bath.

2 Dilute the phage 10^{-4} in buffer.

3 Overlay two plates with 0.1 ml of 10^{-4} dilution with K. Plates (1) & (2).

4 Overlay the other two plates with 0.1 ml of the neat (undiluted) phage suspension with K(P1). Plates (3) & (4).

5 Incubate plates overnight.

</td></tr>
</table>

Day following Part 1

<table>
<tr><td>Part 2
1 hr</td><td>

1 Prepare 8 dilution tubes (4×10 ml; 4×2 ml).
8 soft agar tubes. Place in $46°$ bath.

2 Count plaques on plates (1) to (4) and note restriction on K(P1). (*Do not* stab plates.)

3 Make suspensions of two plaques from the K plates-(1) & (2)-label K1 & K2, and two plaques from the K(P1) plates-(3) & (4)-label K(P1)1 & K(P1)2. (This is done by stabbing a plaque with a sterile, wooden toothpick* and rinsing in 2 ml buffer. Use a fresh toothpick for each plaque.)

4 Dilute each suspension 1/200 (0.05/10) in buffer.

5 Plate 0.2 ml of the neat (undiluted) suspension of K1 and K2 with K(P1). Plates (5) & (6).
Plate 0.05 ml of the dilutions of K1 and K2 with K. Plates (7) & (8).
Plate 0.05 ml of the dilutions of K(P1)1 and K(P1)2 with K. Plates (9) & (10).
Plate 0.05 ml of the dilutions of K(P1)1 and K(P1)2 with K(P1). Plates (11) & (12).

6 Incubate plates overnight.

</td></tr>
</table>

* Alternatively, use a sterile wire and rinse in $\frac{1}{2}$ ml buffer (see Expt.19).

Day following Part 2

Part 3
1 hr

1 Prepare 16 dilution tubes (8×10 ml; 8×2 ml).
16 soft agar tubes. Place in $46°$ bath.

2 Count phage plaques on plates (5) to (12). Note restriction and modification. *Do not* stab the plaques.

3 Make suspensions of one plaque from each plate as in Part 2. Number these suspensions (5) to (12) according to the plate from which they came.

4 Dilute each suspension 1/200 (0.05/10) in buffer.

5 Plate 0.05 ml from the dilutions of plaques (5) to (12) with K. Label plates respectively (13) to (20). Plate 0.3 ml from the neat suspension of plaques (7),(8),(9) & (10) with K(P1). Label plates respectively (21) to (24).
Plate 0.05 ml from the dilution of plaques (5),(6), (11) & (12) with K(P1). Label plates respectively (25) to (28).

6 Incubate all plates overnight.

Day following Part 3

Part 4
½ hr

Determine phage titres on each plate and make a pedigree to illustrate the restriction and modification of phage λ after growth in K and K(P1).

Experiment 24
Unrestricted, low frequency transduction (P22)

Background

In transduction, bacterial genetic material is transferred from one cell to another by means of a vector, which, in its external characters at least, is similar to a phage particle. In *unrestricted* transduction (also called *general* transduction), brought about by phages P1 and P22, a phage-sensitive bacterial strain (*donor*) is infected with the transducing phage under conditions favouring lysis (as detailed on p.8). The phage lysate is then freed from bacterial cells and concentrated by centrifugation. A *recipient* strain, also phage sensitive, but differing genetically from the donor, is now infected with this lysate under conditions favouring lysogenization, and after phage adsorption, is plated on a selective medium. Clones derived from surviving cells possessing newly-acquired characters transferred from the donor parent (at the low frequency of about 1 per 10^5 to 10^6 infected cells) can then be selected from the large background of parental recipient cells.

Intention

In this experiment, the recipient strains are a series of phenotypically different, tryptophan-requiring auxtrophs of *Salmonella typhimurium* LT2. These bacteria are infected with phage P22 (previously prepared either by lysis of one of these strains, or of the wild-type strain, or of a non-tryptophan auxotroph—see p.8) and plated on minimal medium (without tryptophan). Non-exacting *trp+* (*prototrophic*) colonies produced by transduction are counted after about 48 hr incubation at 37°.

The bacterial recipient strains should be inoculated in broth, in triplicate, 3 days in advance of the experiment. After overnight incubation, 0.1 ml of each culture is spread over a minimal agar plate and incubated for 48 hr. Any culture that gives rise to many more than half a dozen clones (due to back-mutation to prototrophy), should be discarded. Only cultures producing fewer clones than this should be utilized in the experiment.

Reference
DEMEREC M. & P.E.HARTMAN (1959) *Ann. Rev. Microbiol.* **13**, 377.

Requirements

Recipient bacteria
1 ml o/n broth culture $trpB4^-$ (EMG41) in a small tube.
1 ml o/n broth culture $trpC3^-$ (EMG42) in a small tube.
1 ml o/n broth culture $trpD1^-$ (EMG43) in a small tube.

Phages derived from donors
1 ml P22 phage at 10^{11} particles/ml derived from lysis of *ONE** of the following strains: $trpA8^-$ (EMG39) $trpB2^-$ (EMG40)†, $trpB4^-$ (EMG41), $trpC3^-$ (EMG42), $trpD1^-$ (EMG43), $ath5^-$ (EMG44)‡ or wild-type LT2 (EMG36 or 37) (each prepared as in Introduction 7b, p.8).
14 minimal agar (MA) plates.

Method

Part 1
45 min

1 Place the three tubes containing the bacterial cultures in 37° bath. Leave for 10 min to equilibrate to temperature.

2 During this time, spread a 0.1 ml sample from each tube over one MA plate (control for back-mutation to prototrophy of recipient strains). Plates (1),(2) & (3).

3 Spread 0.1 ml of the phage provided over each of two MA plates (control for back-mutation to prototrophy of donor and sterility of phage preparation). Plates (4) & (5).

---

* Each group should use a phage lysate grown on a different donor strain. The first three preparations are also required for Expt. 25.
† In fact, EMG40 is a $trpB2^-met22^-$ strain. However, the fact that the phage carries the $met22^-$ mutation (which is unlinked to the *trp* mutation) will not influence the outcome of this experiment.
‡ Or any other non-trypophan requiring auxotroph (except the linked *cysB* strains).

4 Add 0.1 ml P22 phage (from one of the donors as provided) to each recipient culture. Continue incubation for 10 min to permit phage adsorption to cells.

5 Spread 0.1 ml of each infected bacterial culture over each of 3 MA plates. Plates (6) to (14).

6 Incubate plates for 36 hr.

Two days following Part 1

Part 2

45 min

1 Count all colonies on all plates.

2 Tabulate all class results. After correcting for any small number of colonies growing on control plates 1 to 5, note the following:

(i) Homologous crosses, e.g. (recipient) *trpB4⁻*(x) (donor) *trpB4⁻*, produce no prototrophs.*

(ii) Crosses of mutants with *similar* phenotypes, e.g. *trpB4⁻*(x) *trpC3⁻*, yield prototrophs which are not strikingly fewer in numbers than those from crosses of mutants with *dissimilar* phenotypes, e.g. *trpB4⁻*(x) *ath5⁻*, or with the wild-type donor, e.g. *trpB4⁻*(x) WT.

(iii) Crosses of mutants with *identical* phenotypes, viz. *trpB4⁻*(x) *trpB2⁻*, give a significant number of prototrophs, but strikingly fewer than from all other *productive* crosses.

Conclusions

Supposing the experiment had utilized a large number of phage lysates, each prepared on an independent *trpB⁻* strain, and in all cases the results of transduction between *any* pair of different *trpB* mutants gave rise to colonies in numbers significantly higher than those of the control, what would this tell you about the *trpB* gene?

Note the lack of reciprocity in crosses (e.g. compare *trpB4⁻*(x) *trpC3⁻* with *trpC3⁻*(x) *trpB4⁻*) and the need for more precise methods for mapping.

---

* Crosses are denoted by first quoting the genotype of the strain used as the *recipient*, followed by the symbol (x), then followed by the genotype of the *donor* strain of bacteria which was lysed in the preparation of the phage used to infect the recipient.

Experiment 25

(a) Linked transduction and linear order of sites
(b) Abortive transduction

Background

(a) *Linked transduction*

In the P22-Salmonella system, since the transduction frequency is low (*c.* 1 per 10^5 phage-infected cells) the joint transduction of two characters is unlikely to result from two independent transductional events (*c.* 1 in 10^{10}) and can arise only as a result of simultaneous transfer of two markers on the same fragment of the donor genome by a single vector. *Joint* (*linked* or *co-*) transduction is thus evidence of close linkage. In general, this is rarely observed, thus indicating a considerable degree of fragmentation of the recipient genome. Since the DNA content of a P22 phage particle is only about 1% that of the *S.typhimurium* chromosome, it is likely that each transduced fragment will be less than 1% of the entire genome.

One example of joint transduction in Salmonella involves the four loci controlling tryptophan biosynthesis and *one* of a series of loci controlling cysteine synthesis (*cysB*). If phage from a wild-type (WT) donor is used to infect a double auxotroph carrying any *trp⁻* marker together with a *cysB⁻* marker, prototrophic clones derived by joint transduction of the wild-type alleles of both markers can be selected by plating on MA. In addition, clones resulting from independent transduction of the *cysB⁻* and *trp⁻* markers appear on MA supplemented with either tryptophan (MA + trp) or cysteine (MA + cys) respectively. If the donor is a phenotypically-distinct tryptophan auxotroph, a variety of phenotypes can be selected, and the numbers of the various classes which appear can be used to map the relative order of the loci with precision (three-point test) (see Fig. 6, p.117).

(b) *Abortive transduction*

For reasons not yet known, the majority of auxotrophic, recipient bacteria which receive fragments of donor chromosome carrying wild-type alleles, fail to incorporate them by recombination to yield prototrophic transductants. Instead, the donor fragments, which do not multiply but can express their function, are transmitted unilinearly, i.e. to only one daughter cell at each bacterial division. The result is an extremely limited amount of growth since, at any given time, only a single bacterium in the clone carries a functional gene. This phenomenon, known as 'abortive transduction', offers a means of performing complementation tests as an adjunct to transductional analysis (OZEKI, 1956).

References
CLOWES R.C. (1964) 'The Bacteria', Volume 5, p.253, eds: I.Gunsalus & R.Y.Stanier, Academic Press: London.
OZEKI H. (1956) *Carneg. Inst. Wash. Publ.* **612**, 97.
OZEKI H. (1959) *Genetics*, **44**, 457.

Intention

The experiment utilizes a *trpD⁻cysB⁻* recipient which is infected with phage grown on a *trpA⁻* (or a *trpB⁻*) donor. Selection for various transductional classes arising from crossings-over at various points within the region, permit the ordering of the three loci.

In addition, the fact that the mutation in the donor has taken place in a functional unit distinct from either of those mutated in the recipient, is shown by the presence of 'minute colonies' due to complementation.

As a prerequisite for this experiment, preparations of P22 phage grown on each of the three Salmonella strains *trpA8⁻*, *trpB2⁻* and *trpB4⁻* at concentrations of about 10^{11} particles/ml, are required, as is an overnight broth culture of the double-mutant strain *trpD11⁻cysB18⁻* (EMG48) (or *trpD10⁻cysB12⁻*, i.e., EMG49) previously screened for back mutation as in Expt.24 (p.109). In this instance, however, independent back mutation of either locus is checked by pre-plating on MA supplemented either with cysteine (for mutation to *trp⁺*) or with tryptophan (for *cys⁺*).*

---

* The broth used to culture strain *trpD⁻cysB⁻* should be supplemented with 20 μg/ml cysteine. Some broths are deficient in this amino acid, which imposes selection in favour of any *cys⁺* revertants that may arise.

Requirements

Part 1   *Recipient (bacteria)*—2 ml o/n broth* culture of a $trpD^-cysB^-$ strain (EMG48 or 49).

                  Donor (phage)—0.2 ml P22 phage lysate at 10^{11} pfu/ml grown on $trpA8^-$ (or $trpB2^-$ or $trpB4^-$).†

                  2 MA plates‡—label (1) & (2).
                  2 MA + cys plates‡—label (3) & (4).
                  2 MA + ind plates‡—label (5) & (6).
                  2 MA + trp plates‡—label (7) & (8).
                  2 MA + ind + cys plates‡—label (9) & (10).

Part 2   4 MA plates—label (11),(13),(15) & (18).
                  2 MA + cys plates—label (12) & (19).
                  3 MA + ind plates—label (14),(16) & (20).
                  1 MA + trp plate—label (17).
                  1 MA + cys + ind plate—label (21).
                  Replicating block.
                  4 replicating velvets.

Method

Part 1   1 Place the tube with 2 ml recipient bacteria in 37°
$\frac{1}{2}$ hr   bath.

             2 After 10 min for temperature equilibration, add 0.2 ml of the phage provided.

             3 After a further 10 min to allow phage adsorption, spread 0.1 ml samples on each of the 10 plates provided, *avoiding an area of 1 cm from the periphery of the plate* (transduction plates).††

             4 Incubate plates overnight (not more than 18 hr).

---

* See footnote on previous page.
† Different groups in the class should use different lysates (also required at same concentration for Expt.24, p.110).
‡ As a class control, eight plates of each type are required for control platings.
†† As a class control, plate 0.1 ml of the uninfected bacteria and 0.1 ml of each phage in duplicate, on a similar series of plates (control plates).

Experiments 26 and 27
Colicinogeny

Background

The ability of a bacterial strain to produce a protein-like antibiotic known as a colicin is dependent upon the presence of a genetic factor known as a colicinogenic factor (*col*). Colicinogeny has many similarities with lysogeny, but the genetic factor, which can be shown to be DNA, is not structurally associated with its lethal protein product, the colicin, nor does it normally appear to be integrated into the bacterial chromosome. Some colicin factors are infective and give rise to a system of conjugation similar to that produced by the *F* sex factor (see Expts. 28 to 32, p. 128 *et seq*). Cultures of some stably colicinogenic strains give rise to a low efficiency system of conjugation and transfer (low frequency-colicinogeny transfer; LFCT, or LFC), but cultures which have been newly infected with the factor have an enhanced efficiency of transfer (high frequency-colicinogeny transfer; HFCT, or HFC).

Reference
SMITH S. & B.A.D. STOCKER (1960) *Brit. Med. Bull.*, **18**, 46.

Experiment 26
Inhibition and resistance in colicinogeny

Intention

The following experiment demonstrates the sensitivity and development of resistance of bacterial strains to the action of colicins.

Requirements

Part 1   Stock nutrient agar (NA) plates streaked for single colonies of the following strains:
EMG45: *S.typhimurium* LT2*cysD*36⁻(*colI*)⁺
EMG46: *S.typhimurium* LT2*cysD*36⁻(*colE2*)⁺
EMG47: *S.typhimurium* LT2*cysD*36⁻(*colI*)⁺(*colE2*)⁺
EMG35: *E.coli* K94(*colV2*)⁺
1 NA plate.

Part 2   1 small tube molten soft agar in 46° bath.
1 ml o/n broth culture strain EMG1 (*E.coli* K12 *met⁻col-s*).
1 ml o/n broth culture strain EMG20 (*E.coli* K12 *met⁻colE-r*).

Method

Part 1   **1** Mark the plate on the back in quadrants.
15 min   **2** With a straight wire, stab an inoculum from each of the four strains EMG45,46,47 and 35 centrally into each quadrant of the NA plate.

3 Incubate for 24 hr.

Day following Part 1

Part 2
2 periods of
5 min
separated
by 45 min

1 Invert the plate top downwards on the bench, and place a piece of filter paper in the lid. Add several drops of chloroform to the paper. Replace lid and leave at room temperature for 30 min to sterilize the bacterial growth. Remove filter paper. (Discard lid and use new lid if plastic plate is used.) Incline plate in open-inverted state for 15 min to allow chloroform to evaporate.

2 Add 0.02 ml of culture EMG20 to 5 ml of EMG1 culture (mixed indicator).

3 Add 0.1 ml of this mixed culture to the soft agar tube and overlay chloroformed plate.

4 When overlay has set (15 min), incubate for 18 hr.

Day following Part 2

Part 3
15 min

1 Examine plate for inhibition zones characteristic of *colI* (small, clear), *colE2* (large, turbid) and *colV2* (large, clear). Why does EMG47 produce a complex zone?

2 Reincubate plate for a further 24 to 48 hr.

Two days following Part 3

Part 4
15 min

1 Examine plate for small colonies growing within the inhibition zones. If a colony is picked near to the centre of a zone and purified by restreaking, a culture of these cells will usually now be found to be resistant to the action of the appropriate colicin (*col-r*). In this case if such a culture is used as an overlay to a similar stab plate as in Part 2, it will show no inhibition zone to the appropriate colicin, whilst retaining sensitivity (*col-s*) to the others. (Strain EMG20 was derived as a resistant mutant within an inhibition zone produced by EMG46 in an overlay of EMG1.)

Experiment 27
Kinetics of low and high frequency-colicinogeny transfer in *E.coli*

Background

A system of low frequency-colicinogeny transfer (LFC) involves two strains, a *col+ str-s* donor strain and a *col-r str-r* recipient strain. These strains are mixed, and at intervals after mixing, diluted samples are plated on streptomycin agar to select colonies of the recipient strain. These colonies are then tested for the acquisition of colicinogeny by overlay with a *col-s str-r* indicator strain.

A system of high frequency-colicinogeny transfer (HFC) involves three strains; a *col+ str-s* donor, a *col-r str-s* intermediate and a *col-r str-r* recipient. The donor and intermediate strains are mixed in a 1:20 ratio in nutrient broth and incubated overnight. This culture is then sub-cultured to form a *HFC* mixture in which most of the intermediate bacteria have *recently* acquired the *col* factor; the third (recipient) strain is then added. Samples are then taken at intervals and plated on streptomycin agar to select colonies of the recipient strain which are similarly tested for the acquisition of colicinogeny by overlay with a *col-s str-r* indicator strain.

Intention

These experiments demonstrate LFC and HFC transfer of the colicin factor *colI* in a series of strains which are all derivatives of 58-161F⁻, a methionine-requiring auxotroph of *E.coli* K12. The following strains are required: EMG1 (*colI-s str-r*), EMG17 (*colI+ str-s*), EMG18 (*colI-r str-r*) and EMG19 (*colI-r str-s*).

For convenience both LFC and HFC experiments can be initiated on the same day.

---

* This is to prevent any colonies growing on the surface of the overlay, where they would be dispersed by the indicator overlay (Part 3/3) and obscure the inhibition zones.

Low frequency-colicinogeny transfer—LFC

Requirements

Part 1   1 ml log. broth culture strain EMG17 at about 2×10^8 cells/ml (*E.coli* K12 *met⁻ colI⁺ str-s* F⁻).

1 ml log. broth culture strain EMG18, also at about 2×10^8 cells/ml (*E.coli* K12 *met⁻ colI-r str-r* F⁻).

4 NA + SM (200 μg/ml) plates.

25 ml soft agar (molten at 46°).

100 ml buffer.

6 large tubes.

8 small tubes.

Part 2   2 NA + SM plates.

20 ml soft agar (molten at 46°).

50 ml buffer.

3 large tubes.

4 small tubes.

Part 3   1 ml o/n broth culture strain EMG1.

20 ml soft agar (molten at 46°).

6 small tubes.

Method

Part 1
$6\frac{1}{2}$ hr
with intervals

1 Prepare 6 dilution tubes (4×10 ml; 2×9 ml). Prepare 8 soft agar tubes. Place in 46° bath.

2 Mix 1 ml of EMG17 and 1 ml of EMG18 log. cultures in a small tube and incubate in waterbath at 37°.

3 After 2 hr incubation, take a sample of the mixed culture, dilute 10^{-5} and plate 0.1 ml in duplicate in soft agar on 2 NA + SM plates. When overlays have set (about 10–15 min), overlay with a further *uninoculated** layer of soft agar. Plates (1) & (2).

4 At 6 hr after mixing cultures, take a further sample, dilute, plate and *double* overlay as before. Plates (3) & (4).

5 Leave mixed culture in waterbath at 37° overnight.

6 Incubate plates overnight.

* See footnote on facing page.

Day following Part 1

Part 2
15 min

1 Prepare 3 dilution tubes (2×10 ml; 1×9 ml). Prepare 4 soft agar tubes. Place in 46° bath.

2 Remove plates (1) to (4) to refrigerator.

3 Take further sample of mixed culture 24 hr after mixing. Dilute and plate with double overlay as before. Plates (5) & (6).

4 Incubate plates (5) & (6) overnight.

Day following Part 2

Part 3
$1\frac{1}{2}$ hr

1 Prepare 6 soft agar tubes. Place in 46° bath.

2 Remove plates (1) to (4) from refrigerator to incubator for one hour. All plates should show about 100 small disc-like colonies within the overlays.*

3 Overlay each plate (1) to (6) with soft agar to which has been added 0.1 ml of o/n culture EMG1.

4 Incubate plates overnight.

Day following Part 3

Part 4
$\frac{1}{2}$ hr

1 Count the total number of colonies.

2 Count the total number of colonies showing inhibition zones.

3 Calculate % recipient colonies acquiring colicinogeny after 2,6 and 24 hr.

* If any colonies have broken the surface, remove the growth by gently wiping surface with a filter paper and expose the plate to a short (30 sec) chloroform vapour treatment.

High Frequency-Colicinogeny Transfer—HFC

Requirements

Part 1   1 ml o/n broth culture of strain EMG17.
1 ml o/n broth culture of strain EMG19 (58-161 *met⁻ colI-r str-s* F⁻).
5 ml nutrient broth in ½ oz s/c bottle.
3 large tubes.
50 ml buffer.

Part 2   5 ml log. broth culture strain EMG18.
10 NA + SM plates.
200 ml buffer.
5 ml broth in s/c bottle.
100 ml soft agar (molten at 46°).
15 large tubes.
20 small tubes.

Part 3   2 ml o/n broth culture of strain EMG1.
50 ml soft agar (molten at 46°).
10 small tubes.

Method

Part 1   **1** Prepare 3 dilution tubes (2×10 ml; 1×9 ml).
15 min   **2** Dilute o/n culture of EMG17 to 10^{-3}.
Dilute o/n culture of EMG19 to 10^{-2}.

3 Add 0.05 ml EMG17 dilution and 0.1 ml EMG19 dilution to the 5 ml bottle of broth.

4 Incubate mixture overnight.

Day following Part 1

Part 2
4 hr with
intervals

1 Prepare 15 dilution tubes (10 × 10 ml; 5 × 9 ml). Prepare 20 soft agar tubes. Place in 46° bath.

2 Add 0.1 ml of the o/n mixture to 5 ml fresh broth and reincubate at 37° on turntable rotor for $1\frac{1}{2}$ hr.

3 When total cell concentration is $c.10^8$ cells/ml (total count), add to this mixture 5 ml of a log. culture of EMG18 also at 10^8 cells/ml (total count) and maintain the three-strain mixture at 37° without aeration. (Bottle A.)

Time (min)

0   Immediately take a 0.1 ml sample from Bottle A, dilute 10^{-5} and plate 0.1 ml samples in duplicate in soft agar over 2 NA + SM plates.

15   Plate 2 × 0.1 ml samples of 10^{-5} dilution from Bottle A on 2 NA + SM plates.

30   Plate 2 × 0.1 ml samples of 10^{-5} dilution from Bottle A on 2 NA + SM plates.

60   Plate 2 × 0.1 ml samples of a 10^{-5} dilution from Bottle A on 2 NA + SM plates.

120   Plate 2 × 0.1 ml samples of 10^{-5} dilution from Bottle A on 2 NA + SM plates.

130   Overlay each of the 10 seeded plates with a further layer of *uninoculated* soft agar.

140   Incubate all plates overnight.

Day following Part 2

Part 3
$\frac{1}{2}$ hr

1 Prepare 10 soft agar tubes. Place in 46° bath.

2 Examine all plates.
(If any of the small disc-like colonies have broken through the agar to the surface, remove surface growth and sterilize for 30 sec with $CHCl_3$ as in Part 3/LFC.)

3 Overlay each plate with 0.1 ml of EMG1 in soft agar.

4 Allow 15 min for overlays to set.

5 Incubate overnight.

Day following Part 3

Part 4   **1** Count all colonies, on all plates.

1 hr   **2** Count all colonies showing inhibition zones.

3 Calculate % recipient colonies acquiring colicino-geny at each time.

4. Plot results on graph together with LFC results. A typical result is shown in Fig.7

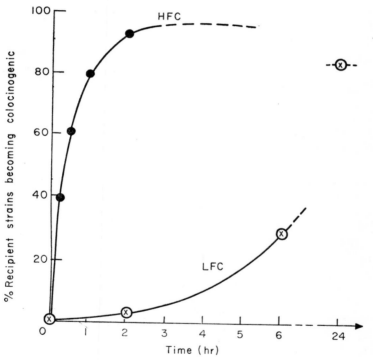

Fig.7 Kinetics of low and high frequency-colicinogeny transfer

Experiments 28 to 32
Conjugation in *E.coli* K-12 mediated by the sex factor F

Background

Conjugation is the only mechanism mediating genetic recombination in bacteria which permits transfer of a large part, and occasionally even the whole, of the chromosome of one parental bacterium to another, so that a complete linkage map can be constructed by recombinant analysis. In addition, it is the only system from which populations of persistent, partially-diploid bacteria ('intermediate males' carrying F-prime factors) can be derived and tests of dominance performed, with respect to many different chromosomal regions.

On the basis of ability to conjugate and transfer genetic material, strains of *E.coli* K12 can be broadly classified into two sexes, 'male' ($\male$) and 'female' ($\female$ or F⁻), which are genetically and physiologically determined. Cultures of $\female$ strains are infertile when mixed; maximum fertility is shown by mixtures of $\male$ and $\female$ strains; mixtures of $\male$ strains are usually poorly fertile. The character of maleness is conferred by a 'sex factor' called F (for 'fertility') which is composed of DNA and determines two sexual functions of the $\male$ bacteria which harbour it:

(1) the ability to form conjugal unions with $\female$ bacteria;
(2) the one-way transfer, from $\male$ to $\female$, of genetic material.

The $\female$ bacteria appear to play no active role in either of these processes.

The factor F exists in $\male$ bacteria in one or the other of two mutually-exclusive states between which it may alternate with low probability (*c*. 10^{-4} per cell generation). In one state (F⁺$\male$), the sex factor is unassociated with the bacterial chromosome and replicates independently of it. In the other state (Hfr $\male$), the sex factor is inserted into the continuity of the circular bacterial chromosome so that the two form a single unit of replication. All $\male$ bacteria, irrespective of the state of the sex factor which they carry, conjugate with $\female$ bacteria with high efficiency. However, the state of the sex factor has a profound influence on the nature of the subsequent genetic transfer.

Properties of F⁺ $\male$ bacteria
(a) On conjugation, the sex factor is transferred with high efficiency to

females, converting them to the F$^+$ ♂ state, so that the character of male-ness spreads like an epidemic through the ♀ population. When young broth cultures of ♂ and ♀ bacteria are mixed, from about 5 to over 90 percent of the ♀ population may be infected with the sex factor in one hour, depending on the particular strains used.

(b) Chromosome transfer is insignificant, recombinants for genes located on the bacterial chromosome appearing with a frequency of less than about 10^{-4}. The fact that any such recombinants arise is due, in part at least, to the presence of small numbers of Hfr ♂ bacteria in the F$^+$ population (see next section).

(c) The sex factor is readily eliminated from F$^+$ ♂ bacteria by growth in the presence of acridine orange. The ♂ bacteria are thereby conver-ted to females.

Properties of Hfr ('high frequency of recombinants') ♂ *bacteria*
(a) On conjugation, the circular bacterial chromosome opens up at a specific point and is transferred, at high frequency, as a linear structure from one particular extremity termed the 'leading locus' or *O* ('origine'). The speed of chromosome transfer is sensitive to temperature variation but is constant under standard conditions, so that the genes enter the ♀ bacteria in the same sequence as their arrangement on the chromosome and at fixed time intervals proportional to their absolute distances from *O*. At 37°, transfer of the whole chromosome occupies about 100 minutes. During transfer, the chromosome tends to break in a random way so that the transfer of genes, and the frequency of their inheritance by recom-binants, fall off exponentially as their distance from *O* increases. This gradient of transfer forms the main basis of mapping by genetic analysis in this system. Unlike all other systems, the gradient is not a function of the frequency of recombination but results from a polarized exclusion of genes from the zygotes.

(b) Hfr ♂ bacteria arise, in F$^+$ ♂ populations, from insertion of the sex factor into the circular chromosome at any one of a considerable (though probably limited) number of sites (see Fig. 9). There is good evidence that this insertion is mediated by a recombination event between a circular sex factor and the circular chromosome which leaves the circularity unimpaired. On conjugation, the chromosome opens up to become lin-ear at the site of sex-factor insertion, the leading extremity (*O*) being determined by the orientation of the sex factor. Thus although all the bacteria in a culture of any particular Hfr isolate behave homoge-neously in transfer, different Hfr isolates from the same F$^+$ strain may transfer the chromosome from different starting points and in opposite directions.

(c) Hfr ♂ bacteria do not normally transfer the *F* factor to females on conjugation. In mixtures, all the non-recombinant ♀ bacteria, as well as all recombinants formed at high frequency, remain ♀. But, if recombinants are selected which inherit the last (terminal) genes to be transferred, and which arise at low frequency due to chromosome breakage, these are frequently found to be Hfr males with the same transfer characteristics as the parental Hfr ♂ strain. Thus, irrespective of the type of Hfr strain, the functional part of the sex factor is always transferred last, at the terminal extremity of the chromosome.

(d) The sex factor of Hfr ♂ bacteria is not eliminated by treatment with acridine orange.

The properties and inter-relationships of F⁺ and Hfr males are summarized in Fig. 8.

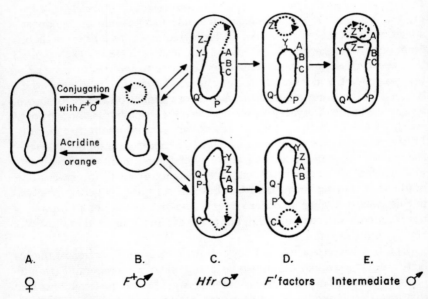

Fig.8 Properties and inter-relationships of F⁺, Hfr and F-prime donors
The interrupted lines represent the bacterial chromosome, and the dotted lines the sex factor, the arrow head indicating the polarity of transfer. The letters A-Z show the locations of various bacterial genes.

F-prime (F′) factors

Hfr ♂ bacteria tend to revert to the F⁺ state, presumably due to reversal of the act of recombination which led to insertion of the sex factor into the chromosome. Occasionally, however, a sex factor is released which has

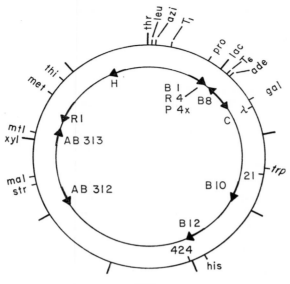

ade = adenine	*mal* = maltose fermentation
azi = sodium azide, resistance or sensitivity	*met* = methionine
	mtl = mannitol fermentation
gal = galactose fermentation	*pro* = proline
his = histidine	*str* = streptomycin resistance or sensitivity
lac = lactose fermentation	
leu = leucine	*thi* = thiamin (vitamin B1)

thr = threonine
trp = tryptophan
T1,T6 = resistance or sensitivity to phages T1 and T6 respectively
Hfr strains: AB = Adelberg; B = Broda; C = Cavalli; H = Hayes; R = Reeves; P4x = Jacob's strain (J2)

Fig.9 The chromosome of *E.coli* K12 and the origin of Hfr strains

1. The figure shows the arrangement and approximate locations on the circular chromosome of a number of commonly used loci, with special reference to those employed in the experiments described. Their designations appear on the outside of the circle. The locations of three prophages (λ,21 and 424) are shown on the inside of the circle.

2. The bold radial projections divide the chromosome into nine segments, each equivalent to 10 minutes transfer time in interrupted mating experiments at 37°. The map and distances between loci are derived from the data of TAYLOR & THOMAN (1964) and indicate the relative locations of the markers with some accuracy.

3. The arrows on the inner circle indicate the leading extremity and direction of transfer of the chromosome of various Hfr strains. Note that the time taken by an Hfr strain to begin to transfer its most proximal marker may exceed by 3 to 4 minutes the apparent distance between the leading locus and the proximal marker as shown on the map. (This extra time is that needed to build a conjugation tube before chromosome transfer can begin.)

incorporated into its structure a fragment of bacterial chromosome. This fragment is usually, though not necessarily, the terminal extremity of the chromosome which was transferred last by the Hfr strain during conjugation (Fig.8). Such substituted sex factors are termed F-prime (F') factors.

When an F' factor is transferred to ♀ bacteria it gives rise to a new type of ♂ which displays some of the properties of both F$^+$ and Hfr males, and so is called an '*intermediate*' ♂. A population of *intermediate* ♂ bacteria not only transfers its F' factor but also its chromosome with the same polarity and general sequence of markers as the Hfr strain in which the F' factor originated, but with rather lower efficiency. However, the first marker to be transferred is now one of the alleles of the gene carried by the F' factor. For example, if the original Hfr ♂ transferred its genes with the sequence AB-Z, an F'-Z^+ factor derived from it, when transferred to a Z^- ♀, promotes chromosome transfer with the sequence $Z^{\pm}$-'AB-$Z^{\mp}$. This is because the intermediate ♂ is heterozygous Z^+/Z^- so that pairing and recombination between the two alleles occurs frequently, leading to rapid alternation between the inserted Hfr and released F$^+$ states (see Fig.8D,E).

Zygotic Induction

When lysogenic Hfr ♂ bacteria, which carry an inducible prophage (such as λ, Fig.9) at a specific chromosomal location, are mated with non-lysogenic females, as soon as the prophage penetrates the ♀ bacteria (zygotes) during chromosome transfer, it enters the vegetative state so that the zygotes are lysed and free phage particles liberated. This is called 'zygotic induction' and does not occur when the ♀ strain alone is lysogenic, nor when both parents are lysogenic and carry the same prophage or distinguishable mutants of it.

Zygotic induction is an important source of perturbation in genetic analysis since it leads to progressive diminution in the number of recombinants inheriting proximal genes, the closer these are linked to the prophage, while the potential to yield recombinants for genes located distal to the prophage is eliminated, since all zygotes containing them are lysed. Zygotic induction is also a valuable tool for studying chromosome transfer itself, because inducible prophages behave as chromosomal markers which are expressed directly on entering the zygote, without the intervention of recombination. Thus, for a given Hfr ♂ strain, the frequencies of zygotic induction for a series of inducible prophages, located at different chromosomal regions (e.g. λ, 21, 424 in Fig.9) indicate directly the frequencies with which these regions are transferred. The fact that the frequency of zygotic induction falls exponentially with the distance of the prophage location from the leading chromosomal extremity, O, shows that the chromosome breaks randomly during transfer. Again, by comparing the frequency of zygotic induction with the frequency with which a proximal marker, closely linked to the prophage site, appears among recombinants in comparable crosses between non-lysogenic strains, an estimate can be made of the probability with which a transferred marker is integrated into a recombinant chromosome ('co-efficient of integration' = c. 0.5).

References

Sexual Differentiation and the Sex Factor, F
HAYES W. (1953) *J. Gen. Microbiol.*, **8**, 72.
HAYES W. (1953) *Cold Spr. Harb. Symp. Quant. Biol.*, **18**, 75.
LEDERBERG J., L.L.CAVALLI & E.M.LEDERBERG (1952) *Genetics*, **37**, 720.

Isolation of Hfr strains
JACOB F. & E.L.WOLLMAN (1956) *C. R. Acad. Sci., Paris*, **242**, 303.
TAYLOR A.L. & E.A.ADELBERG (1960) *Genetics*, **45**, 1233.

The Kinetics of Mating and Chromosome Transfer in Hfr × F⁻ Crosses.
DE HAAN, P.G. & J.D.GROSS (1962). *Genet. Res., Camb.*, **3**, 251.
WOLLMAN E.L., F.JACOB & W.HAYES (1956) *Cold Spr. Harb. Symp. Quant. Biol.*, **21**, 141.
WOLLMAN E.L. & F.JACOB (1958) *Ann. Inst. Pasteur*, **95**, 641.

Zygotic Induction
JACOB F. & E.L.WOLLMAN (1958) *Ann. Inst. Pasteur*, **95**, 497.

The Circular Chromosome
JACOB F. & E.L.WOLLMAN (1958) *Symp. Soc. Exp. Biol.*, **12**, 75.

F-Prime factors
ADELBERG E.A. & S.N.BURNS (1960) *J. Bacteriol.*, **79**, 321.
JACOB F. & E.A.ADELBERG (1959) *C. R. Acad. Sci., Paris*, **249**, 189.

Acridine Orange Curing of the F factor
HIROTA T. (1960) *Proc. Nat. Acad. Sci., Wash.*, **46**, 57.

Experiment 28
F⁺ × F⁻ crosses in *E.coli* K12

Intention

The experiment demonstrates the dependence of mating on the presence of the sex factor, *F*, in one of the parents, as well as the low frequency of recombinant formation in comparison with that of transfer of the sex factor.

1. *Recombinant formation.* Log. broth cultures of an F⁺ and an F⁻ strain *of the same genotype*, both streptomycin-sensitive (*str-s*), are each mixed with a culture of a streptomycin-resistant (*str-r*) F⁻ strain of different genotype and incubated. The mixtures are then washed, and plated on minimal or other selective media on which only recombinant bacteria can grow to yield colonies. The washed mixtures are also diluted and plated on nutrient agar + streptomycin (NA + SM) for colony counts indicating the number of viable F⁻ bacteria present. F⁺ × F⁻ crosses alone yield recombinants, and only at low frequency.

2. F *factor transfer.* Individual colonies of the F⁻ *str-r* strain, selectively re-isolated from both F⁺ × F⁻ and F⁻ × F⁻ mixtures on NA + SM are cultured in separate tubes of broth and then crossed to an F⁻ strain of different genotype, as above. Only those cultures derived from bacteria to which the sex factor was transferred, by conjugation during the initial cross, can yield recombinants. The proportion of originally F⁻ bacteria thus converted (by F⁺ males) to the F⁺ state is high.

Requirements

Part 1 Log. broth cultures, in ½ oz s/c bottles, of each of the following *E.coli* K12 strains, labelled:

  EMG22: F⁺ (*met⁻ str-s*) 5 ml
  EMG14: F⁻ (*met⁻ str-s*) 5 ml
  EMG10: F⁻ (*thr⁻ leu⁻ thi⁻ str-r*) 2 × 5 ml
 2 minimal agar (MA) + thiamin (vitamin B1) at 5 μg /ml + SM (200 μg/ml) plates (MA + B1 + SM).
 4 nutrient agar (NA) + SM (200 μg/ml) plates.

                100 ml buffer.
                8 large tubes.

Part 2   10 ml log. broth culture strain EMG14.
                2 MA + B1 plates (*no* streptomycin added).
                20 ml buffer.
                10 ml broth.
                6 small tubes
                Template for micro-plating technique (see Appendix I, p.234).

Method

Part 1
$\frac{1}{2}$ hr, followed
by a further
$\frac{1}{2}$ hr,
$1\frac{1}{2}$ hr later.

1 Prepare 8 dilution tubes (4×10 ml, 4×9 ml).

2 Mix 5 ml each of cultures as follows:

      $22 + 10$ ($= F^+ \times F^-$)
      $14 + 10$ ($= F^- \times F^-$).

3 Place mixtures in waterbath at $37°$ for $1\frac{1}{2}$ hr. Then centrifuge and resuspend in 5 ml buffer.

4 Spread 0.1 ml of each mixture (undiluted) on MA + B1 + SM for prototrophic recombinants. Plates (1) & (2).

5 Dilute both mixtures 10^{-5} and 10^{-6}. Spread 0.1 ml of each dilution on NA + SM to assess the total number of viable F^- parental cells and to re-isolate clones of these cells in order to test them for inheritance of the sex factor.

Mixture $22 + 10$. Plates (3) & (4).
Mixture $14 + 10$. Plates (5) & (6).

6 Incubate plates (3) to (6) overnight and plates (1) and (2) for 42 to 48 hr.

Day following Part 1

Part 2
½ hr (followed
by 4–5 hr
incubation)
+5 min
(followed by
further 1½ hr
incubation)
+45 min

(A) Recombinant formation

1 Count, by marking on the back of the plates, the total number of colonies arising on plates (3) or (4), whichever contains the higher countable number of colonies. Do not stab the colonies since some are required for sub-culture.

2 Assess the total number of viable F⁻ cells initially present in 1.0 ml of the mating mixture and record the result.

(B) F factor transfer

1 Prepare 6 small tubes containing 1 ml broth.

2 From one of plates (3) or (4), pick 3 well-isolated colonies of the recovered F⁻ strain, and sub-culture each to a separate tube of broth.

3 Similarly pick and sub-culture 3 colonies from plates (5) or (6)

4 Incubate all 6 broth cultures in a waterbath at 37°.

5 When the cultures are markedly turbid (4–5 hr), add to each 1 ml of the log. broth culture of strain EMG14 provided. (Considerable time can be saved in this part of the experiment if a shaking-waterbath is available.)

6 Incubate in waterbath at 37° for 1½ hr.

7 Centrifuge each mixture, wash once in 2 ml buffer, and resuspend in 0.5 ml buffer.
(Since, in these crosses, the presumptive F⁺ donor strain is *str-r* while the F⁻ recipient bacteria, which will constitute the zygotes, are *str-s*, SM cannot be added to the selective medium. Under these conditions cross-feeding and considerable syntrophic growth may obscure or mimic recombinant colonies unless nutrients are thoroughly removed by careful washing.)

8 Using the template provided (Appendix I, p.234), spread *loopfuls* of each mixture, in duplicate, over 2.5 cm diameter areas on MA + B1 plates.

Spread duplicate areas from three colonies derived from (3) or (4). Plate (7).

Spread duplicate areas from three colonies derived from (5) or (6). Plate (8).

(This is a qualitative rest, requiring only a 'yes' or 'no' answer. The technique is economical of material and saves time. The wire loop should have a diameter of roughly 3 mm. For a loopful of adequate volume to be picked up, the loop should be immersed and removed vertically in a plane parallel to the liquid surface.)

9 Incubate the plates 42–48 hr.

Day following Part 2

Part 3
½hr

(A) *Recombinant formation*

1 Examine plates (1) and (2) for the presence of prototrophic recombinant colonies. Count and express in terms of the number of recombinants arising from 1.0 ml of the mating mixture.

2 Assess the recombination frequency, in terms of the number of F^- bacteria yielding one recombinant, from the ratio:

$$\frac{\text{No. prototrophic recombinants per ml mixture (Plate 1)}}{\text{No. viable } F^- \text{ bacteria per ml mixture (Plate 3 or 4)}}$$

3 Record your result for comparison with that of the Hfr $\times$ F^- cross in Expt.29, Part 3A3 (p.143)

Day following Part 3

Part 4
45 min

(*A*) F *factor transfer*

1 Examine the MA + B1 plates (7) and (8), for areas showing prototrophic colonies. Their occurrence shows that the particular isolates of the initially F⁻ bacterium have become F⁺. The number of recombinant colonies per area will probably fall in the range 5–20. Only isolates from the F⁺ × F⁻ cross (Plate 7) should yield recombinants.

2 Correlate the class results: assess the frequency of F transfer in terms of the proportion of F⁻ cells initially present in the F⁺ × F⁻ cross which have been converted to the F⁺ state. Compare this frequency with the frequency with which recombinants are formed.

Conclusions

Using approx. equal population densities of the suggested F⁺ and F⁻ strains, the frequency of recombinants should be about one per 10^4–10^5 ♀ bacteria, while about 50 per cent of the parental ♀ bacteria should be converted to the F⁺ state under the recommended conditions.

Experiment 29

1. Hfr × F⁻ crosses
2. Zygotic induction

Intention

Three crosses are made, involving the same non-lysogenic F⁻ strain but different Hfr strains; the results are compared with respect both to the genetic constitution of the recombinants and to the occurrence of zygotic induction. Two of the Hfr strains (Hfr*H*) differ only in that one is lysogenic for the inducible prophage, λ, while the other is non-lysogenic. The third Hfr strain (Hfr*C*) transfers its loci in the reverse order to Hfr*H* and, although lysogenic, does not show zygotic induction since the λ prophage locus is terminal on its chromosome and is, therefore, transferred to the F⁻ bacteria at only a very low frequency. (For the sequence of transfer of various loci by these Hfr strains, refer to Fig.9, p.131.) Log. broth cultures of the Hfr strains, which are *str-s*, are thoroughly washed to remove free λ phage particles, and diluted 1/10 into fresh broth at 37°. Equal volumes of diluted Hfr suspension and log. broth cultures of the F⁻*str-r* strain are mixed and incubated to allow time for transfer of the proximal part of the chromosome. The mixture is then treated with SM to prevent further multiplication of the Hfr parent and the spontaneous liberation of free λ particles. The treated mixture is finally diluted and plated on minimal or other selective medium for recombinants; it is also plated, together with λ-sensitive, *str-r* indicator bacteria, on NA + SM for 'infectious centres', i.e. zygotes which have received prophage and will lyse to liberate infective phage λ. The recombinants are finally purified and scored for inheritance of unselected Hfr markers.

Requirements

Part 1	5 ml log. broth culture of *one* of the Hfr strains below, washed twice, and *diluted 1/10* in fresh broth at 37°.*

* Different groups will use different Hfr strains.

EMG23 = HfrH(λ)⁻ (Hayes strain: prototrophic, *T1-s lac⁺ T6-s str-s*)

EMG24 = HfrH(λ)⁺ (strain EMG23 made lysogenic for λ phage)

EMG25 = HfrC(λ)⁺ (Cavalli strain: *met⁻ T1-s lac⁺ T6-s str-s*)

5 ml log. broth culture of strain EMG26 (P678 *thr⁻leu⁻thi⁻T1-r lac⁻T6-r* (λ)⁻ *λ-r str-r F⁻*).
(This strain, although non-lysogenic, lacks λ phage receptors and so is resistant to infection by free phage; it can yield infectious centres only by transfer of prophage to it during conjugation.)

5 ml *overnight* broth culture of strain EMG10—a C600 *str-r* (λ)⁻ *λ-s* indicator strain for free phage λ particles (labelled 'I').

2 plates MA + B1 + SM (methionine added for HfrC cross).

2 plates MA + B1 (*without* SM—methionine added for HfrC cross).

2 NA + SM plates (40 ml agar) *kept at 37°*.

1 NA + SM plate.

1 large tube containing 4.5 ml buffer + SM(200 μg/ ml) in 37° bath.

3 large tubes of buffer (1 × 10 ml; 2 × 9 ml) in 37° bath.

2 small tubes containing 3 ml soft agar held molten at 46°.

Waterbath at 46°.

Part 3   3 plates MA + B1 + SM (methionine added for the HfrC cross only).

Part 4   60 small test tubes in rack, sterile, capped.

3 plates MA + SM (methionine added for the HfrC cross).

3 plates MA + B1 + SM (NO methionine; required for HfrC cross only).

3 plates EMB-lactose agar.

1 ml phage T1 suspension at *c.* 10¹⁰ pfu/ml.

1 ml phage T6 suspension at *c.* 10¹⁰ pfu/ml.

100 ml buffer.

7 large tubes.

Method

Part 1
2½ hr

1 Mix the Hfr and F⁻ cultures and incubate in water-bath at 37° for 1 hr.

2 Transfer 0.5 ml mixture to 4.5 ml buffer + SM at 37° (= 1/10 dil) to kill the Hfr bacteria and prevent their spontaneous liberation of phage λ.

3 Maintain inoculated buffer SM solution in water-bath at 37° for 20 min.

4 Further dilute 10^{-2}, 10^{-3} and 10^{-4} in *warm* buffer (= final 10^{-3}, 10^{-4} and 10^{-5} dils) and maintain at 37°.

(A) *To demonstrate genetic recombination*

1 Spread 0.1 ml of the 10^{-3} and 10^{-4} final dils. on MA + B1 + SM (for the HfrC cross this medium supplemented with methionine should be used). Label plates (1) and (2).

2 Spread 0.1 ml of the 10^{-3} and 10^{-4} dilutions on MA + B1 (*without* SM) for approximate viable count of the viable Hfr bacteria; recombinants will also grow on this medium (for the HfrC cross, the medium should be supplemented with methionine).
Label plates (3) and (4).

3 Spread 0.1 ml of 10^{-5} dil on NA + SM for viable count of F⁻ bacteria. Label plate (5).

4 Incubate MA plates (1 to 4) at 37° and NA plate (5) at 30°. The smaller colonies arising overnight at the latter temperature facilitate the counting of large numbers.

(B) *To demonstrate zygotic induction*

1 As soon as possible after diluting the mating mixture (Part 1/4), transfer 0.1 ml of the 10^{-4} and 10^{-5} dils to separate, small tubes containing molten soft agar, in waterbath at $46°$.

2 To each add 5 drops of overnight broth culture of λ-indicator strain labelled 'I', and pour over surface of *warm* NA + SM plates.

3 *Do not replace lids for a few minutes.* When agar layer has set, incubate plates at $37°$ *as quickly as possible* after setting. Label plates (6) and (7).
Note. Since both chromosome transfer and, particularly, the occurence of zygotic induction are very dependent on the mating mixture and the zygotes, respectively, being kept at $37°$, it is most important that this temperature be maintained, so far as is practicable, throughout the above operations. The experiments can be carried out in a $37°$ constant temperature room, with advantage.

Day following Part 1.

Part 2
1 hr

(A) *Hfr* $\times$ *F*$^-$ *cross: genetic recombination*

1 Count the total number of colonies of:
(a) The Hfr parent (Plates 3 and 4) and
(b) The F$^-$ parent (Plate 5).

2 In each case, estimate the total number of viable bacteria initially present in the Hfr $\times$ F$^-$ mixture, and record your result.

(B) *Zygotic induction*

1 Count the number of plaques of phage λ (infectious centres) on plates (6) and (7). The class should compare the results given by the crosses involving the different Hfr strains. Only the cross with strain EMG24 (Hfr$H\lambda^+$) should show a significant number of plaques at the 10^{-4} dilution, since strain EMG25 (Hfr$C\lambda^+$) does not transfer the λ prophage locus at high frequency. Note, however, that plaques may appear which do not arise from zygotic induction but from direct infection of the indicator bacteria.

2 In the case of the Hfr$H(\lambda)^+ \times$ F$^-(\lambda)^-$ cross, assume that all the plaques counted are due to zygotic induction and that it is 100% efficient:

(a) Calculate the number of zygotes per ml of the undiluted mating mixture to which λ prophage was transferred;

(b) From this figure, and from the number of Hfr bacteria per ml mixture (Plates 3 and 4), calculate the percentage Hfr bacteria which transferred the O—λ region of chromosome to zygotes.

Day following Part 2

Part 3
1½ hr

(A) *Hfr cross: genetic recombination*

1 Examine plates (1) and (2). Count, by marking the back of the plates, the number of prototrophic (*thr⁺leu⁺*) recombinant colonies arising fron an appropriate dilution. Do not stab the colonies.

2 Calculate the number of recombinants emerging from 1.0 ml undiluted mating mixture. From this figure, and from the number of Hfr bacteria per ml of mixture (Plates 3 and 4), calculate the percentage of Hfr bacteria which transferred the O—*thr⁺leu⁺* segment of chromosome to zygotes.

3 From the number of recombinants on plates (1) and (2) and the number of F⁻ bacteria per ml (Plate 5), calculate the number of F⁻ bacteria yielding one recombinant and compare the result with that given by the F⁺ × F⁻ cross (Expt.28, Part 3A3). Remember that the ratio ♂/♀ bacteria was 1/1 in the F⁺ cross and 1/10 in the Hfr cross.

(B) *Purification of recombinants for genetic analysis*

1 Touch 60 recombinant prototrophic colonies on plates (1) and (2) lightly with a sterile wire and streak on MA + B1 + SM (for the HfrC cross, this medium should be supplemented with methionine). Twenty colonies can usually be streaked comfortably on a single plate, 10 on each half. Alternatively, the template in Appendix F (p.229) may be used, although the streaks are a bit short. The streaking technique need not aim at producing isolated colonies (though this is desirable), but merely at 'diluting out' contaminating F⁻ bacteria and enriching the prototrophs by a second cycle of growth on selective medium.

2 Label plates (8),(9) and (10) and incubate overnight.

Day following Part 3

Part 4   (A) *Hfr × F⁻ cross: scoring of unselected markers*
1 hr   *among recombinants*

1 Prepare 60 × 1 ml buffer tubes.

2 Pick, with a loop, a small portion of growth furthest from the inoculation site or, preferably, an isolated colony, from each of the 60 streak cultures on supplemented minimal agar (Plates 8,9 and 10).

3 Suspend the growth from each streak in 1 ml buffer, so as to yield a very slight turbidity.

4 Streak a very small loopful of each suspension on each of the following media (20 per plate as before).

(a) *HfrH × F⁻ crosses*:
  (i) MA + SM to score for *thi⁺* (B1⁺) inheritance.
  (ii) EMB-lactose medium, to score for *lac⁺* inheritance.

(b) *HfrC × F⁻ cross*:
  (i) MA + met + SM, to score for *thi⁺* inheritance.
  (ii) MA + B1 + SM, to score for *met⁻* inheritance.

(iii) EMB-lactose medium, to score for *lac⁺* inheritance.

5 In all crosses, the inheritance of sensitivity to phages T1 and T6 from the Hfr parent is then scored by spotting a loopful of suspensions of the phages on the streak inoculum of each recombinant *on the EMB-lactose plates*. Between each spotting, the loop should be flamed and cooled in buffer before recharging with phage, so as to prevent the transfer of bacteria from one streak to another.

6 Incubate plates overnight.

Day following Part 4

Part 5
1 hr

1 From the plates put up under Part 4 score, among the 60 *thr⁺leu⁺* recombinants, the number which have inherited various unselected markers from the Hfr parent. The markers to be scored in the sequence of their arrangement from *O* are as follows:

For the Hfr*H* crosses: *T1-s lac⁺T6-s thi⁺*
For the *HfrC* cross: *T6-s lac⁺T1-s thi⁺met⁻*

Convert these numbers into the *percentage* of *thr⁺leu⁺* recombinants which inherit each unselected Hfr marker.

2 From these results deduce the order on the chromosome of those unselected markers located *distal* to the selected markers. (See diagram under 'Conclusions', below.)

3 Compare the results of the crosses involving the Hfr*H*(λ)⁺ and Hfr*H*(λ)⁻ ♂ strains, and assess the effect of zygotic induction on the inheritance of various unselected markers.

Conclusions

The diagram shows, for the strains HfrH and HfrC, the relationships of the unselected markers to the leading locus O and to the selected markers *thr+leu+*. The interrupted lines indicate, for each Hfr strain, the most distal chromosome region which should not be transferred at significant frequency.

	met^+	thi^+	O	thr^+leu^+	$T1\text{-}s$	lac^+	$T6\text{-}s$		λ
HfrH	· · · · · · · · · · · ◀								
	met^-	thi^+		thr^+leu^+	$T1\text{-}s$	lac^+	$T6\text{-}s$	O	λ
HfrC								▶ · · · ·	
	met^+	thi^-		thr^-leu^-	$T1\text{-}r$	lac^-	$T6\text{-}r$		
P678 F⁻									
				selected markers					

1. In the HfrH crosses no *thi+* recombinants should be found. All the other unselected markers lie on the proximal part of the chromosome and distal to the selected markers. They should show a gradient of inheritance among the recombinants, due to chromosome breakage, in proportion to their distance from *thr+leu+*. Thus among the prototrophic recombinants, about 70% should be $T1\text{-}s$, 40–45% lac^+ and 20–30% $T6\text{-}s$.

2. In the HfrC cross all zygotes generating prototrophic recombinants must have received the O—*thr+leu+* region of chromosome, so that inheritance of unselected markers in this region depends on *recombination* and not on pre-zygotic exclusion. Since recombination occurs frequently in relation to the distances between most of these markers, they will tend to segregate randomly (40–60%), so that it is difficult (or impossible) to map them unambiguously. On the other hand, the frequency of inheritance of *thi+* and *met−*, which lie distal to the selective markers, should show a gradient which permits mapping of their positions relative to *thr leu*.

3. In the cross involving HfrH$(\lambda)^+$, zygotic induction should eliminate all zygotes which receive the O—λ segment of chromosome; but many zygotes will receive shorter segments, due to chromosome breakage, and these will generate recombinants. The closer an unselected marker is located to λ, the more likely it is to be transferred in association with λ and to be eliminated by zygotic induction. Thus the gradient of unselected markers should be steeper in the HfrH$(\lambda)^+$ cross than in the HfrH$(\lambda)^-$ cross where zygotic induction does not occur.

Experiment 30
Interrupted mating: mapping and the estimation of genetic distance as a function of time

Intention

A log. broth culture of an Hfr *str-s* and an F− *str-r* strain, are mixed and incubated at 37°. At appropriate intervals thereafter, samples are removed, diluted, and violently shaken to separate the mating couples.

Appropriate dilutions are finally plated on various media selecting for recombinants inheriting different Hfr markers. The number of recombinants of each class are then counted and plotted on a graph as a function of the time at which the mating was interrupted.

Requirements

Part 1   (*For the whole class*)

5 ml log. broth culture strain EMG27 (HfrBr1), diluted 1/10 in fresh broth at 37° and maintained at 37°.

5 ml log. broth culture of F− strain EMG28 (*pro⁻ thr⁻leu⁻thi⁻str-r*) maintained at 37°.

10 × 100 ml s/c bottles of buffer.

10 × ¼ oz s/c bottles, containing 1.8 ml buffer, and marked 0,5,10,15,20,25,30,35,40 and 50.

(*For each group of students*)

10 small test tubes marked 0,5,10,15,20,25,30,35,40 and 50.

10 plates MA + thr + leu + B1 + SM (marked 'A') to select for inheritance of the Hfr marker *pro⁺*.

10 plates MA + pro + B1 + SM (marked 'B') to select for inheritance of the Hfr markers *thr⁺leu⁺*.

Method

Part 1
1 hr

A single mating mixture is set up, and samples interrupted at intervals thereafter by the supervisor. These samples are then diluted to the plating dilution, and aliquots distributed for plating to each member of the class. If practicable, all these operations are best carried out in a 37° room, to ensure constancy of temperature throughout.

1 5 ml of the (1/10 dil) Hfr broth culture are mixed with 5 ml of the undiluted F⁻ culture in a 1 oz s/c bottle, which is immediately clamped to the periphery of a 33 rpm rotor (see Appendix L, p.238) and incubated at 37°. A stopwatch is started at the time of mixing.

2 Immediately after mixing (0 min) and at 5,10,15,20, 25,30,35,40 and 50 min thereafter, the bottle is *gently* removed from the turntable, and 0.2 ml of the mixture transferred to a ¼ oz s/c bottle containing 1.8 ml buffer (=1/10 dil).

3 The sample to be interrupted is *immediately* attached to a 'Microid' Flask Shaker (or other agitating device, see Note 1b) and vibrated at maximum speed for 30 sec.

4 As soon as the froth has sufficiently subsided (10–20 sec), transfer 1 ml to 100 ml buffer (=10⁻³ final dil).
Shake and dispense c.1 ml amounts into tubes, marked with the time of interruption; one for each group of students.

5 Each group now plates 0.1 ml of each sample, without further dilution, on plates A and B and labels with the time of agitation.

6 Incubate plates for 42 to 48 hr.

Notes
1. The method described here is that used in our laboratory, but there are many variations, such as incubation of the mixture in a flask in a water-bath, which give equally satisfactory results provided three important points are observed:
(a) Since chromosome transfer is very temperature-dependent and is optimal at 37°, every effort should be made to prevent fluctuations of the

mating mixture from this temperature, such as may occur if the mixture is removed periodically from an incubator and cold pipettes are used to remove samples. On the other hand once the samples have been withdrawn, cooling them is not only permissible but advantageous since it inhibits further chromosome transfer, as well as the formation of secondary unions after interruptions.

(b) The use of a 'mixer' or 'blendor' to interrupt the mating is cumbersome and unnecessary. On the other hand, shaking by hand or by holding the sample tube against an eccentrically-rotating rubber stopper or disc driven by an electric motor (e.g. a 'Whirlmixer', see Appendix L), is usually inadequate. An efficient apparatus is described by Low and Wood (1965) *Genet. Res. Camb.* **6**, 300. An alternative to mechanical separation of mating pairs is to treat the samples for 10–15 min with a high multiplicity of phage T6 to which only the Hfr bacteria are sensitive. Adsorption of the phage immediately kills the Hfr bacteria and prevents further chromosome transfer. Subsequent dilution and plating of the samples so reduces the concentration of phage on the plates that the segregation and growth of *T6-s* recombinants is not significantly affected.

(c) To prevent the secondary formation of mating pairs, it is desirable to dilute the samples of mating mixture *before* mechanical agitation, and to make the plating dilution as soon as possible afterwards.

2. Any other combination of Hfr and F⁻ strains may be used, provided that suitably spaced markers are available which can be cleanly selected.

Two days after Part 1

Part 2
45 min

1 Examine the plates spread (in Part 1) with samples from the Hfr × F⁻ cross interrupted at various times after mating.

2 Count the number of *pro⁺* (plates 'A') and *thr⁺leu⁺* (plates 'B') recombinants arising from each time sample.

3 Construct a graph relating the number of recombinants of each class to the time at which the mating mixture was interrupted. Assess the time after mating at which the markers begin to enter the zygotes, by extending the curves back to intercept the time coordinates.

Conclusions

The curves obtained should approximate to those shown in Fig. 10. Strain HfrBr1 begins to transfer the *pro* locus at about 4–5 min and the *thr leu* loci at about 10–12 min after mixing the parental cultures. The plateaux indicate that mating and transfer of a particular Hfr locus are complete in the population. Since HfrBr1 transfers the *thr leu* loci after the *pro* locus, the lower plateau level of *thr⁺leu⁺* recombinants is due to chromosome breakage between the loci during transfer. The slopes of the two curves are determined partly by the rate of pair formation and partly by heterogeneity among the Hfr bacteria in the time required to initiate chromosome transfer after mating (DE HAAN & GROSS, 1962), and actually show the same kinetics.

It is important to note that the curves may fail to show a plateau if equivalent numbers of parental bacteria are mated: before pair formation is complete in the population, unmated bacteria of both parental types will have multiplied, so that the curves continue to rise over a prolonged period.

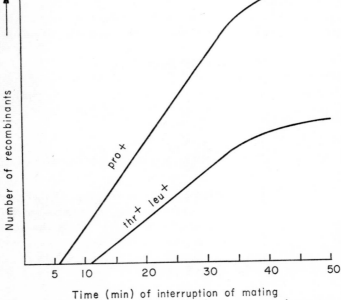

Fig. 10 Kinetics of chromosome transfer in *Escherichia coli*

Experiment 31
The isolation and identification of F-prime (*F'*) factors

Intention

An Hfr *str-s* strain, having a known wild-type gene (Z^+, Fig.8C) located terminally on its chromosome, close to the inserted sex factor, is mated with an F$^-$ *str-r* strain carrying a mutant allele of this gene (Z^-). The mating is interrupted by agitation at a time when only the proximal part of the Hfr chromosome has been transferred. The Hfr population is then killed by treatment with streptomycin. Since mating is stopped long before the Z^+ gene can be transferred as a chromosomal marker, the only Z^+ survivors should be those F$^-$ bacteria which have been infected early by very rare F'-Z^+ factors generated in the Hfr population. Isolation is greatly facilitated by subsequent overnight incubation in fresh broth, which allows infective spread of the F-prime (*F'*) factors through the F$^-$ population prior to plating on selective or EMB-sugar media to identify Z^+ clones. After purification, these Z^+ isolates are distinguished from possible Z^+ Hfr recombinants, and defined as *intermediate males* carrying an F'-Z^+ factor, by their ability to transfer the Z^+ gene at high frequency, in addition to promoting transfer of a proximal chromosomal gene A (Fig.8, D, E).

Requirements

Part 1   5 ml log. broth culture of the Hfr *met$^-$ lac$^+$ str-s* strain Br1 (EMG27) or HfrR4 or HfrP4X. In all these strains the F factor is inserted in the small chromosonal region between the *pro* and *lac* loci (Fig. 9). *pro$^+$* is the first chromosomal marker to be transferred and *lac$^+$* the last. This culture is held at 37°.

5 ml log. broth culture of the F$^-$ strain EMG26 (a *thr$^-$leu$^-$thi$^-$lac$^-$ str-r* strain) held at 37°.

1 large tube or s/c bottle containing 9 ml broth + SM(200 μg/ml).

151

Part 2   6 plates of EMB-lactose + SM agar.
50 ml buffer.
3 large tubes.

Part 3   O/n culture (NA or broth) of the Hfr strain used in
Part 1.
5 plates of EMB-lactose + SM agar.

Part 4   20 ml o/n broth culture of the F⁻ strain EMG29
(*pro⁻try⁻his⁻lac⁻str-r*).
3 plates MA + B1 (label 'A').
3 plates MA + B1 + try + his (label 'B').
50 ml broth.
250 ml buffer.
20 small tubes.
20 large tubes.
Template for micro-plating technique (see Appendix I, p.234).

Part 5   1 to 3 plates EMB-lactose agar, depending on number
of presumptive intermediate ♂ strains isolated.

Method

Part 1   **1** Mix the two 5 ml cultures of strains EMG27 and
45 min   26 provided, return to 37° waterbath for 5 min
and incubate at 37° on a rotor, or with *very gentle*
aeration, for 30 min.

2 Interrupt the mating *thoroughly* by violent agitation (see Note 1(b), p.149).
Dilute the mixture 1 in 10 by adding 1 ml to 9
ml nutrient broth + SM.

3 Incubate diluted culture overnight.

Day following Part 1.

Part 2   **1** Prepare 3×9 ml dilution tubes.
15 min   **2** Make 10^{-1}, 10^{-2}, 10^{-3} dilutions of the incubated overnight mixture in buffer.

3 Spread 0.1 ml of each dilution over two plates of EMB-lactose + SM agar. Plates (1) & (2) (10^{-1}), (3) & (4)(10^{-2}) & (5) & (6) (10^{-3}).

4 Incubate plates 42–48 hr.

Two days after Part 2.

Part 3
45 min

1 All the plates should show confluent growth of non-lactose-fermenting F⁻ bacteria. Examine carefully for papillae, arising from enhanced growth of clones of *lac*⁺ bacteria able to utilize the lactose in the medium. Under these over-crowded conditions the papillae will probably not show the normal colour reaction but will appear as whitish protuberances against the pink background of bacterial growth.

2 With a straight wire, pick 19 papillae and streak each on a quadrant of an EMB-lactose + SM plate so as to obtain genetically pure, isolated colonies. At the same time, streak on one of the quadrants a culture of the Hfr strain used in Part 1, as a control for the next part of the experiment. Plates (7),(8),(9),(10), & (11).

3 Incubate plates overnight.

Day following Part 3.

Part 4
45 min
+ 4–5 hr
incubation
+ 1 hr in-
cubation time
+ 45 min

1 Prepare 20 small tubes of 1 ml broth
   20 × 10 ml dilution tubes.

2 Isolated colonies of *lac+* bacteria, on plates (7) to
   (11), will now appear as darkly pigmented. These
   lac+ isolates are tested in crosses with a *pro−lac−*F−
   strain (strain EMG29) to ascertain whether they
   can transfer both the *pro+* and *lac+* markers at
   high frequency and, therefore, are true intermediate males. The control Hfr strain transfers the
   proximal chromosomal marker *pro+*, but not the
   terminal *lac+* marker, at high frequency. [Remem-
   ber that the *lac+*, presumptively intermediate
   donors you have isolated are derived from a
   thr−leu−lac−str-r F− strain after mating with a
   thr+leu+lac+ Hfr strain. Some may therefore be
   recombinant prototrophs (*thr+leu+str-r*) which can
   be recognized by their ability to grow on unsupplemented MA; however, these cannot be identified
   as donor strains in simple test crosses since they
   cannot be contra-selected in such crosses. Similarly,
   in test crosses, streptomycin cannot be used for
   contra-selection.]
   Pick *one* isolated *lac+* colony derived from each
   papilla, as well as a colony from the control Hfr
   culture, and transfer to separate one ml of broth in
   small tubes.

2 Place all the tubes in the waterbath at 37°.

3 When the cultures are markedly turbid (4–5 hr)
   add to each 1 ml of an overnight broth culture of
   strain EMG29 (*F−pro−try−his−lac−str-r*).

4 Continue incubation in the waterbath at 37° for
   1 hr.

5 Dilute each mixture approx. 10−3 by transferring
   one full 3 mm loopful (see p.137) to 10 ml buffer.
   Mix well.

6 Using the template provided (p.234), spread a full
   3 mm loopful of each diluted mixture over 2.5 cm
   areas on both of the following media:

(a) $MA + B_1$, to recognize prototrophic strains. Plates (12),(13) and (14).

(b) $MA + B_1 + try + his$, to select for pro^+thr^+ leu^+ recombinants inheriting pro^+ from the F' donor and thr^+leu^+ from the recipient strain EMG 29. Plates (15),(16) and (17).

7 Incubate the plates 42–48 hr.

Two days after Part 4.

Part 5
45 min

1 Examine plates (12) to (17). Ignore all lac^+ isolates which produce colonies on *both* plates in the test crossing, implying prototrophic donors. The growth of colonies *only* on $MA + B_1 + try + his$ indicates true pro^+ recombinants derived from matings with presumptive intermediate donors carrying an $F\text{-}lac^+$ factor. This is confirmed for each lac^+ isolate by showing that a high proportion of recombinants derived from it, in contrast to those derived from the control Hfr strain, have also received the lac^+ marker from the donor.

2 Streak 5 pro^+ recombinant colonies from each test cross involving a presumptive intermediate donor, as well as 5 pro^+ colonies from the control Hfr cross, on EMB-lactose agar plates, 20 streaks per plate. Plates (18),(19) and (20).

3 Incubate plates overnight.

Day following Part 5.

Part 6
15 min

Examine plates (18) to (20) and score each group of 5 recombinants for inheritance of the lac^+ character.

Conclusions

Part 1. Success in isolation of intermediate ♂ strains depends primarily on the efficiency with which the mating is interrupted. If an appreciable proportion of Hfr-F⁻ pairs remain unseparated, the whole chromosome may be transferred so that papillae of Hfr lac^+ recombinants arise.

Parts 4 and 5. The majority of lac^+ clones isolated from papillae, although probably carrying an *F-lac+* factor, may be expected to be proto-trophs and unsuitable for further test, producing 1000 or more colonies on both MA plates. Auxotrophic intermediate males should yield about 100–500 *pro+* recombinant colonies on MA + B1 + try + his medium (Part 5).

Part 6. The majority of *pro+* recombinants derived from intermediate ♂ isolates should also have received the *F-lac+* factor and be *lac+*.

The probability that any of the 5 *pro+* recombinants derived from the control Hfr cross will be *lac+* is very low.

Note. This experiment may be presented to classes in an abbreviated form, beginning at Part 4, by providing students with a previously isolated intermediate ♂ strain for identification*. Intermediate ♂ strains tend to be unstable, either losing their F′ factor spontaneously or suffering an exchange of alleles between the F′ factor and the chromosome.

---

* e.g. strain EMG30.

Experiment 32
The elimination of F' factors by treatment with acridine orange

Intention

A broth culture of an intermediate ♂ strain, having a *lac⁻* allele in its chromosome but carrying an *F-lac⁺* factor (i.e. a *lac⁻/F-lac⁺* strain) is highly diluted and a small volume of the dilution (containing 10^3 to 10^4 bacteria) transferred to one ml of the following media:

(a) Broth (control).
(b) Broth + acridine orange.

After overnight incubation the resulting bacterial cultures are plated on EMB-lactose agar to obtain isolated colonies. Whereas all, or virtually all, the colonies emerging from the untreated culture remain *lac⁺*, the majority of those from the culture containing acridine will be *lac⁻*.

Requirements

Part 1   1 ml o/n broth culture of a *lac⁻/F-lac⁺* strain, such as one of those isolated in Expt.31.*
2 small tubes containing 1 ml broth at pH 7.6.
1 small tube containing 1 ml broth at pH 7.6 + acridine orange (50 μg/ml).
(The acridine orange is best made up as a stock solution of 1000 μg/ml in distilled water. Just before the experiment this stock solution is diluted 1 in 20 in broth from which 1 ml is then dispensed. In this experiment *it is very important that the pH of the broth is at 7.6 throughout*.)

Part 2   4 plates of EMB-lactose agar.
100 ml buffer.
6 large tubes.

* Otherwise use strain EMG30.

Method

Part 1 15 min	1 Transfer a *small* loopful (1/500–1/100 ml) of the F′ strain provided to 1 ml broth at pH 7.6.
	2 After mixing well, transfer a similar small loopful to: (a) 1 ml broth (pH 7.6) = control culture (b) 1 ml broth (pH 7.6) + acridine orange = test culture.
	3 Incubate cultures overnight.

Day following Part 1.

Part 2 15 min	1 Prepare 6 dilution tubes (4×10 ml; 2×9 ml).
	2 Make 10^{-4} and 10^{-5} dilutions of the control and test cultures put up in Part 1, and spread 0.1 ml of each over a EMB-lactose agar plate.
	3 Incubate plates overnight.

Day following Part 2.

Part 3 15 min	Examine the plates spread in Part 2 and assess the proportion (if any) of colonies, derived from the control and acridine orange-treated cultures, which reveal the *lac*⁻ genotype. If desired, a log. culture of one of these *lac*⁻ derivatives may be tested for inability to transfer its chromosome by crossing with strain EMG29 (*pro*⁻*try*⁻*his*⁻F⁻) and scoring for *pro*⁺ recombinants, as in Expt.31, Part 4(b).

Experiments 33 to 37
Genetics of *Aspergillus nidulans*

Background

The genetic system of *Aspergillus* forms a bridge between those operating in bacteria and bacteriophage, on the one hand, and higher organisms on the other. As in bacteria, clonal propagation and selective techniques (the chief advantages of microorganisms as tools in genetics) can be used; on the other hand, nuclear structure, nuclear division and the sexual process are essentially the same as in higher organisms.

The important features of the life cycle are illustrated in Figs.11,12 and 13. Colonies consist of an interconnecting network of *hyphae*, the whole network being called a *mycelium*. Hyphae are divided by cross-walls into multinucleate 'cells'.

Conidia. These are asexual spores, and are used for maintaining and transferring cultures. They are haploid, exclusively uninucleate, and about 3μ in diameter. They are 'dry' spores (non-wettable) and remain viable for long periods. Conidia are produced all over the surface of a colony on special aerial hyphae, and the colour of the colony is determined by the pigmentation of the spore wall.

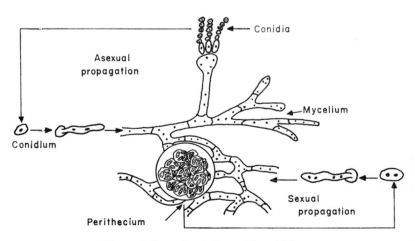

Fig.11 Life cycle of *Aspergillus nidulans*

159

Ascospores. These are the sexual spores. They are found inside large (*c.* 1 mm diameter), black, thick-walled spheres called *perithecia* on the surface of colonies (Fig.11). The details of ascospore development, so far as they are known or inferred, are illustrated in Fig.12. A young perithecium is filled with special hyphae with binucleate cells (Fig.12.1). The two nuclei in one cell fuse to form a diploid zygote nucleus (Fig.12.4), which immediately divides meiotically to form four haploid nuclei (Fig.12.5). The four divide once again, this time mitotically, and the eight daughters are used to make the eight ascospores which are contained in each ascus. One perithecium may contain up to 10^6 ascospores.

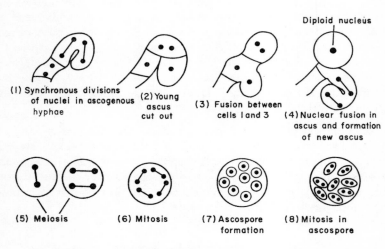

Fig.12 Probable steps in formation of ascospores in Aspergillus

The sexual cycle is essentially the same as that in higher organisms such as man. In each case there is an alternation of haploid and diploid phases, the haploid phase being derived from the diploid phase by meiosis and the diploid phase from haploid by nuclear fusion.

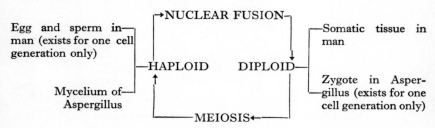

The most important difference between Aspergillus and man from our point of view is that in Aspergillus the somatic tissue (mycelium) can be propagated indefinitely without recourse to sex. This distinction is not strictly valid since human cells can now be maintained in culture.

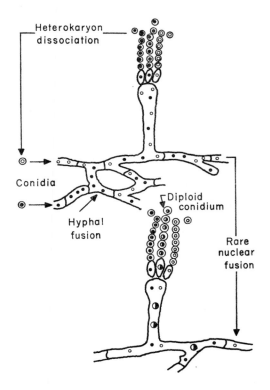

Fig.13 Heterokaryons and diploids in Aspergillus

Heterokaryons and crossing. When conidia from two, genetically-different strains are inoculated together, they may form a common colony (Experiment 37) in which many of the hyphae contain nuclei from both strains as a result of hyphal fusion (Fig.13). A colony of this type is called a *heterokaryon* (a colony derived from one or more genetically-identical conidia is a *homokaryon*). In the perithecia produced by a heterokaryon, nuclear fusion may occur between any two nuclei. Three types of diploid zygote are consequently possible. If the nuclei of the two parent strains are designated *A* and *B*, then the zygotes can be either *AA*, *BB* or *AB*. (Note that Aspergillus is *homothallic*—there are no mating types and fusion between any two nuclei is normally possible.) It is ascospores derived from zygotes of the last type (*AB*) that we are interested in when we make a cross (Experiments 33,34 and 35).

Diploids and mitotic recombination. Very rarely, accidental fusion of nuclei occurs in the mycelium instead of inside the perithecium. The diploid nuclei produced do not immediately undergo meiosis as they would if the nuclear fusion had taken place in an ascus; they are stable and give rise to diploid strains which can be isolated and maintained in the usual way if suitable techniques are available for their detection (Experiment 37).

It is frequently assumed that recombination in higher organisms is confined to the meiotic divisions involved in the formation of the gametes. In the diploid strains of *Aspergillus*, recombination *does* occur at mitosis, although with extremely low frequency. Selective techniques must be employed to detect mitotic recombinants (Experiment 37). Recombination at mitosis can be employed for purposes of genetic analysis, and, in fact, has some advantages over more orthodox techniques. It is now thought that the occurrence of mitotic recombination is not a special feature of *Aspergillus* diploids—it has been found in artificially-synthesized diploid strains of many fungus species and has long been known to occur in Drosophila. Apart from its theoretical importance, mitotic recombination is of great practical importance, since it makes possible genetic analysis and controlled breeding in organisms with no sexual cycle. It also offers, in principle, a short cut in genetic studies of organisms with very long life cycles, such as man, if used in conjunction with tissue culture.

Cultural techniques

1. Optimal temperature for growth is 37°.

2. Cultures are most easily maintained on Aspergillus Nutrient Agar (ANA) slopes (Appendix A25). The conidia are extremely resistant to dessication and will remain viable on the slope long after the agar has dried out completely. More recently, cultures have also been preserved on silica gel (see PERKINS, 1962; OGATA, 1962).

3. Conidial suspensions are made in water to which Tween 80 (0.01% w/v) has been added as a wetting agent (called 'detergent' in protocols). Further dilutions may be made in either detergent or in water.

4. Assays of conidia or ascopores are made as for bacteria. Normally not more than 50 colonies per plate should be aimed for, owing to the spreading growth of the colonies. Colony size can be restricted without interfering with production of conidia by incorporating 0.08% Na desoxycholate (SD) into the medium. Five hundred or more colonies per plate

can be used in this case. With SD, colonies can be replica-plated as for bacteria except that the velvet is used damp to prevent scattering of conidia. More usually a wire replicator is used (see Appendix J) since with velvet the size of inoculum transferred can make scoring difficult.

References

ASPERGILLUS NEWS LETTER, Ed. J.A.Roper, Vols. 1–6.

ELLIOT C. (1960) The cytology of *Aspergillus nidulans. Genet. Res.*, 1, 462.

KÄFER E. (1958) An 8-chromosome map of *Aspergillus nidulans. Adv. Genet.*, 9, 105.

KÄFER E. (1961) The process of spontaneous recombination in vegetative nuclei of *Aspergillus nidulans. Genetics*, 46, 1581.

MACKINTOSH M.E. & R.H.PRITCHARD (1963) The production and replica-plating of micro-colonies of *Aspergillus nidulans. Genet. Res.*, 4, 320.

MORPURGO G. (1963) Somatic segregation induced by p-fluorophenyl-alanine. *Aspergillus News Letter*, 4, 8.

OGATA W.N. (1962) Preservation of *Neurospora* stock cultures with anhydrous silica gel. *Neurospora News Letter*, 1, 13.

PERKINS D.D. (1962) Preservation of *Neurospora* stock cultures with anhydrous silica gel. *Canad. J. Microbiol.*, 8, 591.

PONTECORVO G. & E.KÄFER (1958) Genetic analysis based on mitotic recombination. *Adv. Genet.*, 9, 71.

PONTECORVO G., J.A.ROPER, L.M.HEMMONS, K.D.MACDONALD & A.W.J.BUXTON (1953) The genetics of *Aspergillus nidulans. Adv. Genet.*, 5, 141.

PRITCHARD R.H. (1955) The linear arrangement of a series of alleles of *Aspergillus nidulans. Heredity*, 9, 323.

PRITCHARD R.H. (1960) Localised negative interference and its bearing on models of gene recombination. *Genet. Res.*, 1, 1.

SIDDIQI O.H. (1962) The fine genetic structure of the paba1 region of *Aspergillus nidulans. Genet. Res.*, 3, 69.

Experiment 33
Types of asci in single perithecia

Intention

To make a cross between two auxotrophs, conidia from each are simply streaked together on Aspergillus Minimal Agar (AMA) and the plate incubated for three weeks or more. (N.B. Inadequate aeration favours perithecium production, and plates should be sealed with 'cellotape' or similar material. Mature ascospores are not abundant for 10–14 days, and for class experiments involving crosses, it will usually be necessary to provide a three-week-old heterokaryon.) Since Aspergillus is homothallic (cf. Neurospora, Yeast), three types of ascus can occur in the perithecia produced on a heterokaryon: those resulting from fusion of identical nuclei (AA or BB) and those resulting from fusion of different nuclei (AB). It turns out, as this experiment should show, that all asci in one perithecium are identical, so that instead of saying that a heterokaryon produces asci of three types, we can say that it produces *perithecia* of three types. The inference is that a perithecium develops from a single binucleate cell, and that all asci are ultimately derived from this cell (see Fig. 12).

Requirements

Strain P76 (EMG54) = *bi1*; *w3 ni3*. (See Fig. 14 p. 166 for chromosome map.)

Strain P129 (EMG55) = *pro1 y*; *Acr1*.

(A heterokaryon between these strains with mature perithecia should be provided.)

1 plate Aspergillus Minimal Agar (AMA) (Appendix A23).

1 plate Aspergillus Nutrient Agar (ANA) (Appendix A25).

Method

Part 1
45 min

1 Pick up ten or more perithecia under a low-power binocular microscope ($\times$ 10) with a wire bent at 90° about 0.5 mm from the end and transfer them to a plate of AMA. Try not to choose only large perithecia. Pick them at random.

2 Roll over surface of agar with needle under microscope until they are shining black (to remove adhering conidia and hyphae), taking care not to break perithecia open.

3 Mark the ANA plate with 10 radial lines.

4 Pick up a cleaned perithecium with bent wire or loop and deposit it on wall of petri dish above one of radial lines. Repeat for remaining nine perithecia.

5 Crush each perithecium with sterile glass rod and streak ascospores so released along line with a loop wetted with sterile water.

6 Incubate for minimum of 48 hr.

Two days following Part 1

Part 2   Score each streak for presence of white, yellow and
½ hr   green sectors. Class results should be pooled.

Conclusions

Hopefully, streaks will be of three types. White only (from perithecia in which ascospores were derived exclusively from P76 × P76 matings), yellow only (similarly derived from P129 × P129 matings), and mixed white, yellow, and green with colours in proportions of about 2 : 1 : 1 respectively (derived from P129 × P76 matings). Other results can and do occur.

Possible reasons:
(a) contamination by conidia or perithecial debris;
(b) Perithecia sometimes derived from more than one binucleate cell;
(c) loss of one nucleus from an ascogenous hypha or mis-division in these hyphae.

Note 1. w is epistatic to y and y^+, hence hybrid zygotes $(w/w^+; y/y^+)$ yield the following ascospore types: wy (white), wy^+ (white), w^+y (yellow) and w^+y^+ (green) in equal proportions.

Note 2. On AMA and nutrient media, conidium colour is determined solely by genotype of nucleus it contains. This is why a heterokaryon between spore colour mutants does not have conidia of uniform colour.

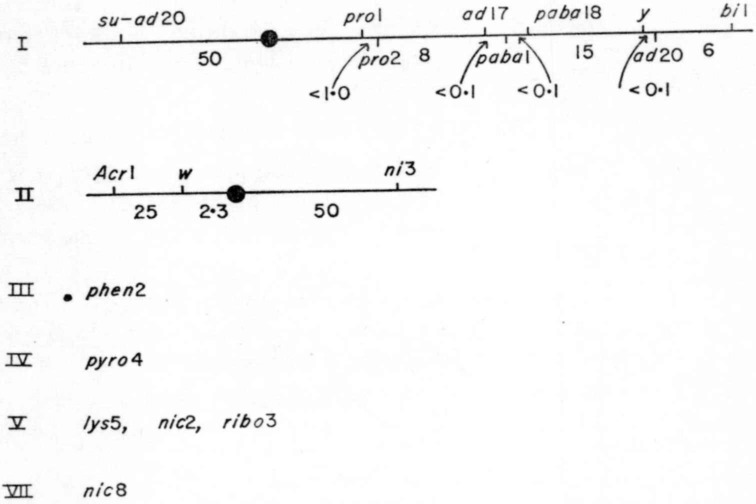

Fig.14 Linkage relationships of markers used in Aspergillus experiments.

The roman figures indicate different linkage groups. The black blobs are centromeres. The arabic numerals show the distance between markers in recombination units.

NOTES: *pro, phen, lys, paba, bi, nic, pyro, ribo, ad*, and *ni* denote requirements for the growth factors proline, phenylalanine, lysine, p-aminobenzoic acid, biotin, nicotinic acid, pyridoxin, riboflavin, adenine and nitrite.

su-ad20 is a recessive suppressor of *ad20*.

y denotes yellow and *w* white spore colour; the *w2* and *w3* mutations (EMG64 & 54) both map at the *w* locus on II.

Acr denotes resistance to acriflavine (dominant to sensitivity). The following mutants are 'leaky'—*ad20, pro*(1 and 2), *ni3: bi1* is not leaky but is readily cross-fed.

Experiments 34 and 35
Measurement of recombination frequencies

Intention

In order to measure recombination frequencies at meiosis in a cross between two strains A and B, it is essential that we score not only colonies coming solely from ascospores, but only those coming from ascospores derived from AB asci. This can be achieved in two ways:

1. We can make use of the fact that the contents of one perithecium are alike (see Experiment 33) and plate from a single perithecium cleaned of conidia and hyphal fragments by rolling. In many cases, it will be necessary to make trial platings from several perithecia, store the suspensions at 4°, and make larger platings from suspensions which prove to be of the AB type.

2. We can make a suspension from large numbers of perithecia without bothering to clean them and plate it on a medium which will not permit either parent to grow. Thus, if one strain requires pyridoxin and the other phenylalanine, we plate on medium lacking both these compounds. Parental-type conidia and ascospores will not grow. Wild-type recombinant ascospores will grow, of course, and these must have come from AB type asci.

The two methods should give identical results if our conclusions from Experiment 33 are correct.

Experiment 34
Plating from a single perithecium ('perithecium analysis')

(It will not be necessary to make trial platings from several perithecia in this experiment, since strains have been chosen which yield a large proportion of hybrid perithecia.)

Requirements

Part 1   Strain P78 (EMG56) = *ad20*; *pyro4*.
Strain P97 (EMG57) = *pro1 paba1 y*; *phen2*.
(A 3-week-old heterokaryon between these strains should be provided.)
1 small tube.
0.5 ml Tween 80 (0.01%).
1 plate AMA.
6 plates ANA + 0.08% sodium desoxycholate (SD).

Part 2   Template (Appendix J, pp.235,236).
3 plates ANA.

Part 3   15 AMA plates supplemented as follows:
3 plates AMA + phen + pro + pyro + paba
('—ad' plates).
3 plates AMA + pro + pyro + paba + ad
('—phen' plates).
3 plates AMA + pyro + paba + ad + phen
('—pro' plates).
3 plates AMA + paba + ad + phen + pro
('—pyro' plates).
3 plates AMA + ad + phen + pro + pyro
('—paba' plates).

Method

Part 1
½ hr

1 Add 0.2 ml detergent to small tube.

2 Pick up one large perithecium and clean as before.

3 Transfer to *wall* of tube, crush with end of glass rod and shake to suspend.

4 Assay number of ascospores/ml by direct microscopic count and make appropriate dilutions to give suspensions containing 10^4 and 10^3 ascospores/ml.

5 Plate (by spreading) 0.1 ml of each dilution on 4 plates ANA + SD.

6 Incubate for minimum of 48 hr.

Two days following Part 1.

Part 2
2 hr

1 Record ratio yellow/green. If you have picked hybrid perithecium, this should be about 1 : 1.

2 Mark the backs of 3 ANA plates at 33 points, using a template (see Appendix J).

3 Inoculate at each point with conidia from a separate colony. To do this, have a plate with colonies face up on bench and a marked, master plate face down. Touch a colony lightly with a bent wire and inoculate upwards at a marked point on the *inverted* master plate, observing the operation through *back* of plate. Have a container with sterile water to hand to cool and wet the wire after sterilization between each operation.

4 Incubate for a minimum of 48 hr.

Two days following Part 2.

Part 3
½ hr

You are now ready to determine the nutritional requirements of the colonies on the master plates by replicating from each of these three master plates onto each type of supplemented AMA plate.

1 Number the master plates and each set of five, supplemented AMA plates 1,2, and 3, and make a reference point on each.

2 Replica plate each master onto a set of supplemented AMA plates using wire replicator (see Appendix J). This should be sterilized by dipping in a glass petri dish containing alcohol and flaming. Replicator is placed 'needles up' on bench and master plate lowered onto it. The replica plates are then lowered onto it in turn.

3 Incubate 24 hr (optimum).

Day following Part 3

Part 4
2 hr

1 Score each colony as + or —. It will be found most convenient to rule 5 columns on lined paper and head them —ad, —phen, —pro, —pyro, —paba. Record + or — against each of the colonies from one dish down the column.

2 Repeat for other plates of the set.

3 Then collect and tabulate your data in the following way:

Class	*pro*	*paba*	*ad*	*phen/pyro* type				Total
				+ +	+ —	— +	— —	
1	—	—	+					
2	+	+	—					
3	+	—	+					
4	—	+	—					
5	—	—	—					
6	+	+	+					
7	+	—	—					
8	—	+	+					
	Total							

4 Pool class results.

5 Check for heterogeneity by X^2.

6 Calculate recombination frequencies and coincidence values.

7 Draw a linkage map. Consult any genetics text for methods.

Note 1. Are allele ratios 1 : 1? If not, why not? (Possibilities are viability differences or contamination by ascospores from 'selfed' asci—how can you distinguish?)

Note 2. It is possible to replicate with velvet instead of wire replicator, providing SD is incorporated in master plates, but scoring may be less easy. The instructor should try both methods himself under local conditions. The intermediate operation of making a master plate is in any case helpful, because scoring replica plates for several characters is confusing when colonies are randomly distributed on plates.

Note 3. Recombination fractions could have been measured directly by plating ascospores on selective media and assaying the number of colonies; *e.g.*, relative numbers on AMA plates supplemented only with phen, pyro, and pro, and on ANA plates would give estimate of *paba-ad* recombination frequency. This method does not allow all classes to be scored, however, and yields less information. It is nevertheless very useful in many circumstances. Owing to very close linkage, few (*c.*0.1%) recombinants between *y* and *ad* will be found. The class can check that *ad*+ colonies are almost exclusively yellow and *ad*− colonies are almost exclusively green and calculate the frequency of exceptions.

Experiment 35
Plating from several perithecia ('selective plating')

Requirements

Part 1   Heterokaryon as for Experiment 34.
                 1 small tube.
                 8 plates AMA + SD + pro + paba + ad.
                 0.5 ml Tween 80 (0.01%).

Part 2   3 plates ANA.

Part 3   3 plates AMA + paba + pro.
                 3 plates AMA + pro + ad.
                 3 plates AMA + paba + ad.

Method

Part 1   **1** Add 0.1 ml detergent to small tube.

½ hr   **2** Transfer ten or more perithecia to tube without cleaning

         3 Crush *en masse* with sterile rod (end of spreader or needle). Add further 1 ml detergent, shake to suspend and count titre. (Take care to count only ascospores; these can be distinguished from conidia since they are red and larger.)

         4 Make appropriate dilutions to give suspensions containing approximately 5×10^4 and 5×10^3/ml.

         5 Plate 0.1 ml of each suspension on four supplemented AMA plates.

         6 Incubate plates for a minimum of 48 hr.

Two days following Part 1.

Parts 2,   As for Experiment 34. In this case, however, you have
3 and 4   selected for *pyro*+ *phen*+ recombinants and therefore
            have to score only for *pro*, *paba*, and *ad*. Compare
            results with Experiment 34.

Experiment 36
Mapping within a cistron and localized negative interference

Intention

In this experiment, we shall see if two mutants, *pabaI* and *pabaI8*, obtained independently from wild type, are located at the same or different sites on the chromosome. The mutants do not complement each other (a diploid, heterozygous *pabaI/pabaI8* requires paba for growth) and are therefore located in the same cistron.

The experiment should also illustrate another feature of recombination, *localized negative interference*, which has been found in a number of organisms.

Four crosses will be used:

(a) *pabaI* × *pabaI8*;	(b) *pabaI* × *pabaI*;
(c) *pabaI8* × *pabaI8*;	(d) *adI7* × *pabaI*.

Two platings will be made from (a),(b), and (c), one on medium without paba to assay for *paba⁺* recombinants or back-mutants, and one on a medium lacking a nutritional factor required by each parent to assay for the proportion of viable ascospores which come from hybrid asci.

Requirements

Part 1   *Mature heterokaryons:*

(a) Strain P138(EMG58) = *pro2 pabaI8 biI*; *phen2*; *lys5*
Strain P112(EMG59) = *adI7 pabaI y*

(b) Strain P112(EMG59) = *adI7 pabaI y*
Strain P87(EMG60) = *proI pabaI*; *nic8*

(c) Strain P115(EMG61) = *pabaI8 biI*
Strain P117(EMG62) = *pro2 pabaI8 y*

(d) Strain P112(EMG59) = *adI7 pabaI y*
Strain P254(EMG63) = *proI biI*; *AcrI*; *pyro4*.

Plates:
Cross (*a*) 6AMA + SD + pro + ad + bi + phen + lys
8AMA + SD + pro + paba + bi + lys

> *Cross (b)* 6AMA + SD + pro + ad + nic
> 8AMA + SD + pro + paba
> *Cross (c)* 6AMA + SD + pro + bi
> 8AMA + SD + paba
> *Cross (d)* 8AMA + SD + pro + ad + bi.

150 ml molten soft agar (held at 46°)(Appendix A11).
50 small tubes.

Part 2   *Cross (a)* 3 plates AMA + pro + bi + phen + lys
Cross (d) 3 plates AMA + pro + bi.

Method

Part 1
½ hr
each cross

1 Prepare 42 soft-agar tubes. Place in 46° bath.

Crosses (a),(b), and (c)

2 Dispense 0.05 ml detergent into 3 small tubes.

3 Collect large numbers of perithecia from each cross and transfer them to a small tube.

4 Crush perithecia, add additional 2 ml detergent to suspend, and determine ascospore titre. Your counts should be at least 10^7/ml in each case. If your titre is sufficiently high, decant into a fresh tube to remove bulk of perithecial debris. If not, collect more perithecia before doing this.

5 Dispense 0.3 ml of each suspension into 3 tubes of soft agar and 0.1 ml into three more.

6 Overlay on plates appropriate to cross (lacking paba in each case).

7 Dilute suspension to 5×10^4 and 5×10^3 ascospores/ml and add 0.1 ml from each to 4 tubes of soft agar.

8 Overlay on plates appropriate to cross (supplemented with paba).

Cross (d)

9 Make ascospore suspension in a small tube in usual way and dilute to give suspensions containing about 5×10^4 and 5×10^3 spores/ml.

10 Spread 0.1 ml of each dilution onto 4 plates.

11 Incubate all plates 48 hr minimum.

Two days following Part 1.

Part 2
(*a*) & (*d*)
crosses—
1 hr each
(*b*) & (*c*)
crosses—
15 min each

1 Count colonies and record colour ratios on all plates not overcrowded.

2 Estimate frequency of *paba*+ colonies from (*a*),(*b*), and (*c*) in the following way:

If ascospore titre in cross (*a*) was 2.4×10^7/ml

Dilution	Plated (ml)	Medium	Mean No. of colonies/plate
0	0.3	—paba	69
0	0.1	—paba	24
10^{-3}	0.1	+paba	59
10^{-4}	0.1	+paba	7

On the +paba plates we have selected *ad*+ *phen*+ recombinants. The two loci are unlinked; consequently, $\frac{1}{4}$ of all viable ascospores from hybrid asci will be recombinants of this type.*

Hence number of hybrid ascospores in initial suspension is:

$$4 \times 59 \times 10^3 \times 10 = 2.36 \times 10^6/\text{ml}$$

0.1 ml of this suspension gave 24 *paba*+ colonies. The frequency of these is therefore:

$$24 \times 10/2.36 \times 10^6 = 1.0 \times 10^{-4}$$

The proportion of these *paba*+ colonies which might be attributable to back mutation can be estimated from the number (if any) of *paba*+ colonies in crosses (*b*) and (*c*).

3 We now want to classify the *paba*+ colonies from (*a*) and also from (*d*) as *ad*+ or *ad*-. This can be

---

* *N.B.* In cross (*c*) the number of ascospores of this type will be 10 times the number of colonies since *paba* and *bi* are linked and recombine with a frequency of 0.2. Difficulties may be experienced in this cross owing to cross-feeding and growth of *bi*- colonies. Instructors could isolate a recombinant *paba18 bi1 nic2* from a cross between P12 and P115 for use in (*c*) instead of P115.

done by marking the back of one or more AMA plates, supplemented as indicated under 'Requirements', at 33 points using template and inoculating upwards as before with a bent wire. You will thus be able to score up to 99 colonies from each cross as *ad⁺* or *ad⁻*.

4 Incubate plates for 24 hr.

Day following Part 2.

Part 3   *Cross (a) and (d)*
½ hr   Record colonies as *ad⁺* or *ad⁻*.
for each
cross

Conclusions

The order of *paba1* and *paba18* with respect to *y* will be apparent from y/y^+ ratio among *paba⁺* recombinants in (*a*). This order will be confirmed by the ad^+/ad^- ratio. Thus if order is *ad-paba1-paba18-y*, the cross can be written:

$$
\begin{array}{ccccc}
+ & + & paba18 & + \\
\hline
ad17 & paba1 & + & y
\end{array}
$$

and the majority of *paba⁺* recombinants will be *ad⁺ y*. Colonies which are *ad⁻* or *y⁺* are multiple recombinants and the frequency of these can be estimated and compared with the frequency expected on the basis of the results from cross (*d*). The proportion of *ad⁻* colonies in (*d*) gives the recombination frequency between *ad17* and *paba1*. The proportion of yellow colonies gives the recombination frequency between *paba1* and *y*. You will find that recombination between the two *paba* mutants is associated with a higher rate of recombination between *ad* and *paba* and also between *paba* and *y*, than expected from the values found in cross (*d*), in previous crosses (Experiments 34 and 35) and, in the case of *ad* and *y*, from control platings in (*a*). This effect has been called *negative interference*.

An appropriate modification to the protocol would also permit you to show that this interference is localized. To do this, you could score *paba*⁺ recombinants as *pro*⁺ or *pro*⁻ and *bi*⁺ or *bi*⁻. You would then be able to determine the recombination frequency between *pro* and *ad* and between *y* and *bi*. The values obtained should be compared with corresponding values obtainable either from the control cross (*d*) or, better, from the control plating from cross (*a*).

Experiment 37
(a) Synthesis of heterokaryons
(b) Isolation of diploids
(c) Detection of mitotic recombination

Background

(a) To obtain stable heterokaryons with a high proportion of heterokaryotic hyphae, it is necessary to inoculate the two strains together on a medium which will permit neither strain to grow by itself. Thus, if one strain requires riboflavin and the other lysine for growth, and the two are inoculated together on AMA, neither strain can grow alone, but the two can cooperate and grow together since each can synthesize the compound required by the other. Heterokaryons made in this way are said to be 'balanced' or 'forced'. If one attempts to make a heterokaryon by simply inoculating the two strains together on ANA, the resulting mixed colony will contain only a very small proportion of heterokaryotic hyphae.

(b) If conidia from a 'balanced' heterokaryon between two auxotrophs are harvested and plated on AMA, no colonies will appear. The reason for this is that conidia are exclusively uninucleate and the heterokaryon is dissociated into its two components (see Fig.13). If the harvested conidia are plated at high density on AMA, however, a few colonies do appear. Some of these are heterokaryons resulting either from contamination of the conidial suspension with mycelial fragments, or from synthesis of new heterokaryons on the plate. Some of them, however, turn out to be stable diploids heterozygous for the nutritional characters of the two parents and, hence, prototrophic.

(c) Heterozygous diploid strains, although stable, show rare segregation at mitosis. Segregants are of two types (a) haploid and (b) diploids homozygous for markers for which the parent diploid was heterozygous. Diploids arise from either (i) mitotic crossing-over which leads to homozygosis for all markers from the point of exchange to the distal end of the chromosome arm or (ii) 'non-disjunction' which leads to homozygosis for all markers on the chromosome involved. The distribution of genotypes among *haploids* can be used to determine whether two markers are on the same or different chromosomes. The distribution of genotypes among *diploid* segregants can be used to map loci relative to the centromere of the chromosome on which they lie.

179

Intention

This experiment is designed to provide instruction on synthesizing and handling diploid strains. The literature should be consulted for details of techniques for mapping and marker localization through mitotic segregation.

Requirements

Part 1 Large tube containing 2 ml solid ANA.
Strains: P12(EMG64) = *ad20 bi1*; *w2*; *ribo3 nic2*
    P20(EMG65) = *su-ad20 y ad20*; *Acr1*;
       phen2; *lys5*.

Part 2 Sterile filter paper in petri dish.
2 plates AMA + ad.

Part 3 4 plates AMA + ad.
1 plate ANA.

Part 4 4 plates ANA.
4 plates AMA + ad.
$\frac{1}{2}$ oz s/c bottle.
30 ml molten soft agar at 46°.
8 small tubes.
Low power binocular microscope.

Part 5 4 plates ANA.
4 plates AMA + phen + lys + rib + nic + bi.
$\frac{1}{2}$ oz s/c bottle.

Part 6 Low power binocular microscope.

Method

Part 1
15 min

1 Cover ANA in test tube with sterile water (1 ml).

2 Flame loop, cool in sterile water, brush gently over surface of one strain to pick up conidia, and transfer these to tube.

3 Repeat for second strain.

4 Stir mixture very gently to mix conidia but try to avoid sinking them below the surface.

5 Incubate overnight (not longer).

Day following Part 1.

Part 2
15 min

1 Pick up and remove felt of mycelium in tube with sterile loop.

2 Drain off surplus liquid by placing on sterile filter paper and transfer to centre of an AMA + ad plate.

3 Tease out and distribute small lumps (about 7) of felt around the plate.

4 Repeat with remaining material on second plate.

5 Discard unused felt.

6 Incubate plates for 2–3 days.

Three days following Part 2.

Part 3
15 min

1 Examine plates for sectors showing rapid growth.

2 With a wire, cut out small blocks of agar from growing edges of sectors and transfer to fresh plates (4 of AMA + ad and 1 of ANA). Place blocks close to margin, about 4 per plate.

3 Incubate for 4 days.

Four days following Part 3.

Part 4
45 min

You should now have good heterokaryons on AMA +ad plates. If not, it may be necessary to repeat procedure in Part 3 using plates inoculated in Part 2.

1 Examine under dissecting microscope and note distribution of colour. Compare with ANA plate.

2 Prepare 8 soft agar tubes. Place in 46° bath.

3 Add 5 ml sterile detergent to the screw-cap bottle.

4 Harvest conidia from heterokaryons with a loop until you have a thick suspension in the bottle. (Take care not to scrape loop too hard over colonies, so as to avoid picking up mycelium.)

5 Shake suspension vigorously.

6 Spin down (4 min in bench centrifuge at top speed) and resuspend in water (2 ml).

7 Assay by microscopic count — your suspension should have at least 2×10^7 conidia/ml.

8 Add appropriate amount of suspension to 4 soft agar tubes to give at least 10^7 conidia/tube and plate each on AMA + ad.

9 Make appropriate dilution of suspension and dispense an appropriate quantity of this dilution into 4 soft agar tubes to give $c.50$ conidia/tube. Plate each on ANA.

10 Incubate plates (48 hr minimum).

Two days following Part 4.

Part 5
45 min

1 Count colonies on ANA plates. Estimate from this the number of conidia plated on AMA.

2 Count number of green colonies on AMA plates (irregular colonies with mixture of yellow and white heads will be re-formed heterokaryons) and calculate frequency.* The green colonies will be

---

* Note that clonal distribution of diploids will lead to wide fluctuations in this frequency from experiment to experiment—*c.f.* Expt.3, p.22.

diploids. (Check by measuring conidium diameter under microscope using micrometer eyepiece previously calibrated. Haploids have diameter of 3μ and diploids about 4μ. It is preferable to measure length of chains of 3 or more conidia to reduce error.)

3 Make suspension of conidia from one green colony and dilute to give about 10^4/ml. Place 1 loopful at 8 to 10 points on the supplemented AMA plates provided.

4 Dilute further and plate to give about 20 colonies/plate on ANA.

5 Incubate for 4 days.

Four days following Part 5.

Part 6
½ hr

Examine AMA plates for sectors of wild-type growth.*

Examine colonies on ANA for spots of white or yellow.†

---

* *ad20* is leaky and gives wispy colonies with no conidia. Sectors on AMA with full growth and conidia are haploids carrying *su-ad20* or homozygotes (*su-ad20/su-ad20*). This is a selective method for isolating segregants (see also use of p-fluorophenylalanine as alternative—MORPURGO, 1963). We are selecting for *su-ad20* haploids and *su-ad20/su-ad20* diploids. Their classification with respect to ploidy and other segregating markers can be carried out by isolating single sectors, purifying them, and determining their nutritional requirements by replica-plating. Note that white segregants will be almost exclusively haploid, since diploids of this type would require coincidence of two more events (one on chromosome I and one on chromosome II). This double selection for *w*: *ad*+ segregants is therefore a selective technique for isolating haploid segregants.

† These are either homozygotes (*w/w* or *y/y*) or haploids (*w* or *y*). If you wish to differentiate them and examine their genotype, it will be necessary to pick off individual white or yellow heads under a low-power binocular microscope using a sharpened tungsten wire (see Appendix J) and streak them out on ANA plates for further purification and classification. The white diploids should be almost all prototrophs since none of the other nutritional markers are on chromosome II with *w*. The yellow diploids will be either *ad*+ (*su-ad20/su-ad20*) originating by non-disjunction, or *ad*− (originating by mitotic crossing-over between *y* and its centromere). Haploids (*w* or *y*) can carry all combinations of markers possible by segregation of whole chromosomes (*i.e.*, combinations like *phen*− *lys*− are possible, but combinations like *ribo*−*lys*− and *ribo*−*nic*+ should not occur since these would require coincidence of mitotic crossing-over and haploidization).

Appendix A
Media

(In the preparation of all media, distilled water should be used.)

1. Nutrient Broth (Broth)

Oxoid No.2 nutrient broth powder	25 g
Water	to 1000 ml

Dissolve broth powder in water
Dispense in appropriate s/c bottles.
Autoclave at 15 lb for 15 min.
pH: 7.4 to 7.6.

2. Nutrient Agar (NA)

Oxoid No.2 nutrient broth powder	25 g
Davis New Zealand agar powder	12.5 g
Water	to 1000 ml

Suspend agar and broth powder in water
Steam at 100° until dissolved (1½ hr for 12 litres).
Dispense into s/c bottles (500 ml).
Autoclave at 15 lb for 20 min.
pH: 7.4 approx.

3. Water Agar ($\times 4/3$ concentrate)

Used as solidifying agent for minimal agar with Minimal Salts ($\times 4$) (see No.4), and with E.M.B. nutrient base (see No.8) for E.M.B. agar (see No.10).

Davis New Zealand agar powder	20 g
Water	to 1000 ml

Suspend and steam at 100° until dissolved (2 hr for 12 litres).
Adjust pH to 7.2 (this is most important to prevent hydrolysis).
Dispense 75 ml or 300 ml volumes into 100 ml or 400 ml bottles respectively.
Autoclave at 15 lb for 20 min.

4. Minimal Salts ($\times 4$ concentrate)

NH_4Cl	20 g
NH_4NO_3	4 g
Na_2SO_4 anhydrous	8 g
K_2HPO_4 anhydrous	12 g
KH_2PO_4	4 g

$MgSO_4 . 7H_2O$ 0.4 g

Water to 1000 ml

Dissolve each salt in cold water in the order indicated, waiting until previous
  salt is dissolved before adding next (a light precipitate will be formed).
Filter into 25 ml or 100 ml bottles.
Autoclave at 15 lb for 15 min (no further precipitate should be formed).
pH: 7.2.

5. 20% **Glucose** ($\times$ 100 concentrate)

D-Glucose 200 g

Water to 1000 ml

Dissolve in warm water.
Dispense into bottles (100 ml).
Autoclave at 5 lb for 10 min.
Also applies for:

maltose	lactose	D-galactose
D-xylose	D-mannitol	L-arabinose

6. *Liquid Minimal Medium (MM)

Minimal salts ($\times 4$) (see No.4)	25 ml or	100 ml
20% Glucose (see No.5)	1 ml	4 ml
Sterile water	to 100 ml	400 ml

Mix three components under aseptic conditions just before use.

7. *Minimal Agar (MA)

Water agar (see No.3)	300 ml or	75 ml
Minimal salts ($\times 4$) (see No.4)	100 ml	25 ml
20% Glucose (see No.5)	4 ml	1 ml

Melt agar at 100° or by autoclaving at 15 lb for 15 min.
Add warmed, sterile salts and glucose. Media is now ready to dispense in plates.

N.B. Supplements should be added at the following concentrations:

amino acids	20 μg/ml (of L-form)
vitamins	1 μg/ml
†streptomycin	200 μg/ml.

*These media are made up immediately before use, either as liquid culture media
or in order to pour plates.

† Note. This concentration of streptomycin is adequate for all purposes where
the intention of the experiment is to prevent growth of streptomycin-sensitive
bacteria (it will be abbreviated to SM). However, in experiments on virulent phage
(p.68 to p.90) where streptomycin is added to kill phage-infected bacteria and
prevent formation of infective centres, a concentration of 2000 μg/ml is usually
added, and this will be abbreviated to 'Strep'.

8. E.M.B. Nutrient Base

Difco 'Bacto' casamino acids	42.5 g
Difco 'Bacto' yeast extract	5.25 g
NaCl	27 g
K₂HPO₄	10.5 g
Water	to 1000 ml

Dissove in the order indicated.
Dispense into 75 ml bottles.
Autoclave at 15 lb for 15 min.

9. E.M.B. Dyes (× 100 concentrate)

Eosin yellow	4 g	Methylene blue	0.65 g
Water	to 100 ml	Water	to 100 ml

In each case, weigh dye out directly into final container and add water.
Autoclave at 15 lb for 15 min.
(Dyes obtainable from George Gurr Ltd., London S.W.6.)

10. *E.M.B. Agar

Water agar (see No.3)	300 ml
E.M.B. nutrient base (see No.8)	75 ml
20% Sugar (see No.5)	20 ml
Eosin yellow (× 100) (see No.9)	4 ml
Methylene blue (× 100) (see No.9)	4 ml

Melt agar at 100°, or by autoclaving at 15 lb for 15 min.
Add warmed, sterile base, sugar and dyes.
Agar is now ready to dispense in plates.

11. Soft Agar

Difco 'Bacto' agar powder	6 g
Water	to 1000 ml

Steam at 100° for 1 hr.
Dispense into bottles (50–100 ml.)
Autoclave at 15 lb for 15 min.
pH: 7.0.

* See footnote to p.185.

12. M9 Salts ($\times$ 10 concentrate)

Na_2HPO_4 anhydrous	60 g
KH_2PO_4 anhydrous	30 g
NaCl	5 g
NH_4Cl	10 g
Water	to 1000 ml

Dissolve in order indicated.
Dispense into 100 ml bottles.
Autoclave at 15 lb for 15 min.

13. *M9 Medium

M9 Salts ($\times$ 10) (see No.12)	100 ml
20% Glucose‡	20 ml‡
0.1M $MgSO_4$†	10 ml
0.01M $CaCl_2$†	10 ml
Sterile water	to 1000 ml

Autoclave each solution separately (15 lb for 15 min).
Mix all components aseptically just before use.

14. Buffer

Na_2HPO_4 anhydrous	7 g
KH_2PO_4	3 g
NaCl	4 g
$MgSO_4.7H_2O$	0.2 g
Water	to 1000 ml

Dissolve each salt in the order given, before adding next.
Dispense in 100 ml s/c bottles.
Autoclave at 15 lb for 15 min.

* See footnote to p.185.
† These solutions are also used in the preparation of phage buffer (A17).
‡ When M9-glycerol medium is required, replace 20 ml glucose with 10 ml 20% glycerol (see Experiments 11 and 12).

15. Phage Broth

Difco 'Bacto' peptone	15 g
Oxoid tryptone broth powder	8 g
NaCl	8 g
Glucose	1 g
Water	to 1000 ml

Dissolve in order shown.
Dispense into appropriate s/c bottles.
Adjust pH to 7.2.
Autoclave at 15 lb for 15 min.

16. T-phage Nutrient Agar (TNA)†‡

Oxoid tryptone broth powder	10 g
Difco 'Bacto' agar powder	10 g
NaCl	8 g‡
Glucose	1 g
Water	to 1000 ml

Suspend agar and nutrients in water.
Steam at 100° (1½ hr for 12 litres).
Dispense into s/c bottles (500 ml).
Autoclave at 15 lb for 15 min.
pH: 7.0.

17. Phage Buffer

Na_2HPO_4 anhydrous	7 g
KH_2PO_4 anhydrous	3 g
NaCl	5 g
$0.1M$ $MgSO_4$*	10 ml
$0.01M$ $CaCl_2$*	10 ml
Water	to 1000 ml

Dissolve first three components in order indicated. Then add prescribed volumes of next two sterile solutions.*
Autoclave at 15 lb for 15 min.
Dispense into appropriate s/c bottles.

† When streptomycin is added to TNA to prevent phage-infected bacteria developing as infected centres, a concentration of 2000 μg/ml is used, and is abbreviated to 'Strep TNA'.
‡ When 'salt-free' TNA is specified (e.g. Expt.13) the medium is made up omitting the NaCl.
* These solutions are also used in the preparation of M9 medium (A13).

18. Subtilis Minimal Salts (SMS) ($\times 4$ concentrate)

Ammonium sulphate	8 g
K_2HPO_4	56 g
KH_2PO_4	24 g
Sodium citrate. $2H_2O$	4 g
$MgSO_4.7H_2O$	0.8 g
Water	to 1000 ml

Dissolve in order indicated.
Autoclave 15 lb for 15 min.
Dispense into appropriate s/c bottles.

19. *Subtilis Minimal Medium (SMM)†

SMS ($\times 4$) (see No.18)	100 ml
20% Glucose (see No.5)	10 ml
0.8% sterile Casein hydrolysate	10 ml
Sterile water	to 400 ml

Mix aseptically.

20. *Subtilis Minimal Agar (SMA)

Water agar (see No.3)	300 ml
SMS ($\times 4$) (see No.18)	100 ml
20% Glucose (see No.5)	20 ml

Melt agar at 100° or by autoclaving at 15 lb for 15 min.
Add warmed sterile salts and glucose.
Agar is now ready to dispense in plates.

21. Nutrient Agar Slopes

Difco 'Bacto' nutrient broth powder	15 g
NaCl	5 g
Difco 'Bacto' agar powder	12.5 g
Water	to 1000 ml

Dissolve agar in water by steaming.
Add and dissolve other ingredients.
Dispense 2.5 ml into ¼ oz bijoux bottles.
Autoclave at 15 lb for 15 min.
Allow to set in a sloping position.

* See footnote to p.185.
† Used in producing competant cultures.

22. Stab Medium

Difco nutrient broth powder	0.9 g
NaCl	0.5 g
Difco 'Bacto' agar powder	0.75 g
Water	to 100 ml

Dissolve agar in water by steaming.
Add and dissolve other ingredients.
Autoclave at 15 lb for 15 min.
Dispense aseptically into sterile tubes† under u.v. hood.
Cap aseptically under u.v. hood. (Tubes are pre-sterilized by heat overnight. Caps sterilized in absolute alcohol.)

23. Aspergillus Minimal Agar (AMA)

$NaNO_3$	6.0 g
$MgSO_4.7H_2O$	0.52 g
KCl	0.52 g
KH_2PO_4	1.52 g
$FeSO_4$ ⎤ $ZnSO_4$ ⎦	trace (1 crystal)
Davis New Zealand agar powder	15 g
Water	to 1000 ml

Dissolve the agar by autoclaving.
Add other ingredients.
Adjust pH with *N* NaOH to approximately 6.5.
Autoclave at 15 lb for 10 min.
Supplement with 10 ml 20% glucose (see No.5) before use.

24. Aspergillus Minimal Salts Solution ($\times 4$ concentrate)

If large quantities of Aspergillus minimal medium are required and particularly if other media for growth of *E.coli* (No.3 & 4 etc.) are being used, it may be found more convenient to make up a salt solution at 4 times strength as follows, which may be then used in conjunction with water agar (No.3) as an alternative to No.23 (AMA) above.

KH_2PO_4	15.2 g
$NaNO_3$	60 g
$MgSO_4.7H_2O$	5.2 g
KCl	5.2 g

† Suitable tubes are $\frac{1}{2}$ dram vials obtained from Camlab (Glass), Cambridge. Alternatively, small (50×15 mm) tubes with aluminium screw caps and rubber liners may be used. These capped tubes, obtainable from Hiller (p.243), are autoclavable and will be found to be generally more convenient.

$$\left.\begin{array}{l} \text{FeSO}_4 \\ \text{ZnSO}_4 \end{array}\right\}$$ trace (1 crystal)

Water   to 2500 ml

Dissolve in order indicated.
Adjust pH to 6.5.
Dispense into appropriate s/c bottles.
Autoclave at 15 lb for 10 min. (*N.B.* The slight precipitate after autoclaving is normal, and need not be removed.)

25. Aspergillus Nutrient Agar (ANA)

Difco 'Bacto' yeast extract	1.0 g
Difco 'Bacto' peptone	1.0 g
NaNO$_3$	6.0 g
Difco 'Bacto' casamino acids	1.0 g
Davis New Zealand agar powder	15.0 g
Adenine	0.15 g
Vitamin solution (see No.26)	10 ml
Water	to 1000 ml

Dissolve the agar by autoclaving.
Add other ingredients.
Adjust pH to 6.0.
Dispense into appropriate s/c bottles.
Autoclave at 15 lb for 10 min.

26. Aspergillus Vitamin Solution

Biotin	0.01 g
Pyridoxin HCl	0.01 g
Aneurin HCl (thiamin)	0.01 g
Riboflavin	0.01 g
p-Aminobenzoic acid	0.01 g
Nicotinic acid	0.01 g
Water	to 100 ml

Dissolve and autoclave at 15 lb for 10 min.

This solution should be kept in the dark, as the riboflavin is photolabile. Any of the vitamins included above may, of course, be omitted if strains needing this vitamin are not being used.

27. Supplements for Aspergillus Minimal Medium

For growth of nutritional mutants, Aspergillus minimal medium should be supplemented with:

Vitamins	1 μg/ml
L-Amino acids	50 μg/ml
Adenine	100 μg/ml

It is convenient to carry stock solutions of the separate vitamins and amino acids at 100 times the final concentration required (adenine is insoluble at this concentration but can be made soluble by the addition of an equivalent amount of HCl).

Appendix B
Key to strains used in experiments

The following abbreviations are used for the genetic characters of the strains shown in this table and throughout the text.

ara, gal, lac, mal, mtl and *xyl* stand for the sugars arabinose, galactose, lactose, maltose, mannitol and xylose; a + (superscript) for fermentation, a − (superscript) for non-fermentation. *ath, bio, cys, his, ind, leu, met, pro, thi, thr, thy, trp, tyr* stand for growth requirements of adenine + thiamin, biotin, cysteine, histidine, indole, leucine, methionine, proline, thiamin, threonine, thymine, tryptophan and tyrosine; a + (superscript) for non-requirement, a − (superscript) for requirement.

str and *azi* stand for the inhibitors streptomycin and sodium azide; *-s* stands for sensitivity to these drugs, *-r* for resistance. T_1 to T_7 are phages; *-s* stands for strains sensitive to these phages, *-r* for resistance.

col stands for colicin; colicins of various kinds are known denoted by capital letters, viz. I, E_2; production of these colicins denoted by a + (superscript), nonproduction by − (superscript), sensitivity by *-s*, resistance by *-r*. λ, P_1, P_{22} stand for temperate phages; a + (superscript) for their production, a − (superscript) for non-production, *-s* for sensitivity and *-r* for resistance (*def* stands for defective phage).

su indicates suppressor mutation. RC is a gene controlling ribosomal synthesis, *-rel* indicates relaxation state, *-str* the stringent state.

Please note that certain different genetic symbols are used in Aspergillus (see Fig.14 p.166).

The contributors to this book cannot undertake to provide the bacteriophage, bacterial or fungal strains advocated for use in the experiments described, nor is it likely that many of the laboratories listed in the International Registry (Appendix C) hold more than a few of these strains.

The Curators of the following Collection Centres have kindly agreed to maintain the recommended stocks and to supply them on request, in accordance with their usual charges and other conditions of issue. The strains may be requested under the 'EMG' numbers given in this Appendix.

Bacteriophage and Bacterial Strains

National Collection of Industrial
  Bacteria
Ministry of Technology
Torry Research Station
P.O.Box No.31, 135 Abbey Road
Aberdeen, SCOTLAND

American Type Culture Collection
12301 Parklawn Drive
Rockville, Maryland 20852
UNITED STATES OF AMERICA

Aspergillus nidulans Strains

The Curator
The Culture Collection
Commonwealth Mycological Institute
Ferry Lane
Kew, Surrey, ENGLAND

Fungal Genetics Stock Center
Department of Biological Sciences
Dartmouth College
Hanover, New Hampshire 03755
UNITED STATES OF AMERICA

EMG reference number of strain	Genotype	Synonym(s)	Used in Experiment Number(s)	Catalogue Number (Appendix CI)
1	Escherichia coli K12 met^- str-r F^-	58-161F$^-$	3*,7,26,27	004
2	,, ,, ,, 'wild type'	K12 or K(λ)	1,2,16,17	004
3	,, ,, ,, $trpA^-$	KF51		
4	,, ,, ,, $trpB^-$	KF52	5	
5	,, ,, ,, $trpC^-$	KF53		
6	,, ,, ,, $trpD^-$	KF54		
7	,, ,, ,, thi^-	2000		008
8	,, ,, ,, $lac^-(i^+z^+y)thi^-$	20S0	11	008
9	,, ,, ,, $lac^-(i^-z^+y)thi^-$	3300		008
10	,, ,, ,, $lac^-(i^+z^+y)thr^-leu^-thi^-(\lambda)^-str$-$r$ F^-	C600	1,11,21,23,28,29	008
11	,, ,, ,, F'-$lac^+(i^+z^+)$	A'327	12	005
12†	,, ,, ,, $lac^-(i^-z^-)F^-$	2320	12	005
13	,, ,, ,, prototrophic λ-r $su1^+$	CR63	18	
14	,, ,, ,, $met^-(\lambda)$-λ-r F^-	W1655F$^-$	1,21,28	004
15	,, ,, ,, $thr^-leu^-thi^-(\lambda def)$	P14	21	
16	,, ,, ,, $thr^-leu^-thi^-lac^-(\lambda)$-$(P1)^+$ F^-	C600(P1)$^+$	23	004
17	,, ,, ,, $met^-(colIb)^+F^-$	RC519	27	006
18	,, ,, ,, met^-colI-r str-r F^-	RC510	27	006
19	,, ,, ,, met^-colI-r F^-	RC547	27	006
20	,, ,, ,, met^-colE-r str-r F^-	RC511	26	006
21	,, ,, ,, met^-F^+	58-161F$^+$	21	004
22	,, ,, ,, $met^-(\lambda)$-λ-r F^+	W1655F$^+$	28	004
23	,, ,, ,, Hfr (Hayes) prototrophic $(\lambda)^-$		29	004
24	,, ,, ,, Hfr (Hayes) prototrophic $(\lambda)^+$		29	004
25	,, ,, ,, Hfr (Cavalli) met^- $(\lambda)^+$	HfrC	29	004

For notes see p.196.

EMG reference number of strain	Genotype	Synonym(s)	Used in Experiment Number(s)	Catalogue Number (Appendix CI)
26	*Escherichia coli* K12 thr⁻leu⁻thi⁻lac⁻T1-r T6-r (λ)⁻λ-r str-r F⁻ met⁻	P678 F⁻	29,31	004
27	,, ,, ,, Hfr (Broda 1) met⁻	HfrBr1	30†,31‡	004
28	,, ,, ,, pro⁻thr⁻leu⁻thi⁻str-r F⁻		30	004
29	,, ,, ,, pro⁻trp⁻his⁻lac⁻str-r F⁻	J62 str-r F⁻	31,32	004
30	,, ,, ,, thr⁻leu⁻thi⁻lac⁻str-r(F-lac⁺)	W945(F-lac⁺)	31,32	005
31	*Escherichia coli* B 'wild-type'	B	10,13–18	011
32	,, ,, ,, str-r	B/S	13,14,16	011
33	,, ,, ,, T2-r	B/2	16	011
34	,, ,, ,, thy⁻	B3	8	016
35	*Escherichia coli* K94 (colV2)⁺	K94	26	018
36	*Salmonella typhimurium* LT2 'wild'	LT2	19,22,24	023
37	,, ,, str-r	RC920	20	023
38	,, ,, (P22)⁺	LT2 (P22)⁺	20	023
39	,, ,, trpA8⁻		4,6,24,25	023
40	,, ,, trpB2⁻met22⁻		24,25	023
41	,, ,, trpB4⁻		4,6,24,25	023
42	,, ,, trpC3⁻		4,6,24	023
43	,, ,, trpD1⁻		4,6,24	023
44	,, ,, ath5⁻		24	023
45	,, ,, cysD36⁻(colIb)⁺	RC902	26	026
46	,, ,, cysD36⁻(colE2)⁺	RC906	26	026
47	,, ,, cysD36⁻(colIb)⁺(colE2)⁺	RC905	26	026
48	,, ,, trpD11⁻cysB18⁻		25	023
49	,, ,, trpD10⁻cysB12⁻		25	023

For notes see p.196.

EMG reference number of strain	Genotype	Synonym(s)	Used in Experiment Number(s)	Catalogue Number (Appendix CI)
50	*Bacillus subtilis ind+tyr+*	SB19	9	001
51	,, ,, *ind-tyr+*	168	9	001
52	,, ,, *ind+tyr-*		9	001
53	,, ,, *ind-tyr-*		9	001
54	*Aspergillus nidulans biI; w3 ni3*	P76	33	402
55	,, *proI y; acrI*	P129	33	402
56	,, *ad20; pyro4*	P78	34,35	402
57	,, *proI pabaI y; phen2*	P97	34,35	402
58	,, *pro2 pabaI8 biI; phen2; lys5*	P138	36	402
59	,, *adI7 pabaI y*	P112	36	402
60	,, *proI pabaI; nic8*	P87	36	402
61	,, *pabaI8 biI*	P115	36	402
62	,, *pro2 pabaI8 y*	P117	36	402
63	,, *proI biI; acrI; pyro4*	P254	36	402
64	,, *ad20 biI; w2; ribo3 nic2*	P12	37	402
65	,, *su-ad20 y ad20; acrI; phen2; lys5*	P20	37	402

The lack of symbols assumes wild-type characteristics. For example, *E.coli* K12 strains can be assumed to require no growth factors, to be sensitive to all T phages, all drugs such as streptomycin and all colicins, and to ferment all carbohydrates, to be lysogenic for phage λ and to adsorb it (λ-s), unless denoted otherwise. (See Appendix D, p.223)

* Or any other *T6-s* K12 strain.

‡ Other appropriate Hfr strains such as HfrP4x or Hfr Reeves 4 may also be used.

† Note. This strain has a 'polar' mutation in the *z* gene, which results in lack of expression of the *y* gene as well, so that neither β-galactosidase nor permease are produced.

Appendix C
International registry of microbial genetic stocks

1 The following international registry of microbial genetic stock strains is intended initially to provide only the basic needs of teaching and research and was compiled by Dr. William Hayes under the auspices of the International Cell Research Organisation (ICRO). The strains are maintained by laboratories actively engaged in teaching and research as a voluntary cooperative venture. Requests for strains for teaching purposes should be addressed in the first instance to a laboratory in the nearest geographical area. These requests should be modest and every effort should be made to maintain and perpetuate any strains received, so that repetitive requests are not made. Any difficulties in obtaining strains should be addressed to the appropriate author (p.xi).

2 The registry comprises three documents:

I is an alphabetically arranged list of strains so far available, classified under the headings *Bacteria, Bacteriophages* and *Fungi*, in which each item is given a catalogue number.

II gives the names and addresses of all those who have agreed to cooperate in this scheme, classified into eight geographical regions (allotted numbers 1–8) and listed by countries within these regions (designated by the first two letters of the country). Finally, each contributor is given a reference number.

III is a table from which, within any geographical area, the provider of any particular strain can be read off. As in document I, the table is classified under *Bacteria, Bacteriophages* and *Fungi*.

Suppose you live in Western Europe (region 2) and want the single-stranded DNA phage φX174. From document I, under *Bacteriophages, virulent*, you find that this phage has the catalogue number 215. From table III, *Bacteriophages*, the intersection of row 215 and column 2 (Western Europe) identifies the regional providers of this phage by the codes WG2, WG5, IS1, IT1, NL1, NL2. If you live in West Germany (WG), you can see from document II that the phage is obtainable locally fron Dr. Hofschneider, Munich or Dr. Vielmetter, Tübingen.

3 This present information is deficient in many ways, but it is hoped that it will prove useful and will get the scheme 'off the ground'. The system of cataloguing is flexible so that the registry can be considerably expanded without much trouble. It is suggested that information regarding extension of strains held by present participants, or the addition of further laboratories to the list, should be sent to Dr. Hayes (1.UK3) so that a revised registry may be issued whenever the occasion demands.

Bacteria	Catalogue number
Bacillus subtilis	
Wild type & auxotrophic mutants for transformation	001
Transducing phages for	002
Phages with DNA infectious for (by transformation)	003
Escherichia coli	
Strain K-12.	
Limited stocks of mutants & sexual types (Hfr,F$^+$,F$^-$) for conjugation experiments	004
Carrying F-prime (F′) factors	005
Carrying colicin (*col*) factors	006
Carrying resistance transfer factors (RTF)	007
With mutations (y,z,i) in *lac* operon	008
Radiation-sensitive/resistant mutants of	009
Partial diploids of	010
Other strains.	
B, wild type	011
B/r (+ phages P1*bc* & P1*bt* for transduction), F$^+$, Hfr & F′ sexual types	012
C, wild type	013
C, mutants, F$^+$ and Hfr strains	014
ML, carrying *lac* mutations as follows:	015
ML30, *lac*$^+$($i^+z^+y^+$)	
ML308, *lac*$^+$($i^-z^+y^+$)	
ML35, *lac*$^-$($i^-z^+y^-$)	
Various: thymine-requiring, wild type & auxotrophs.	016
'relaxed' for RNA synthesis (*rel*)	017
Colicin-producing strains, various	018
Pasteurella pestis and *pseudotuberculosis* auxotrophs	019
Proteus mirabilis	
Genetic stocks	020
Mutants + transducing phage	021
Pseudomonas aeruginosa	
P$^+$ and P$^-$ auxotrophs for conjugal crosses	022

	Catalogue number
Bacteria (*contd.*)	

Salmonella (usually *Salm.typhimurium*)
Limited mutant stocks (+ phage P22) for transduction
    experiments   023
Unlimited mutant stocks for research   024
Hfr strains of   025
Carrying colicin (*col*) factors   026
Carrying resistance transfer factors (RTF)   027

Serratia
Genetic stocks   028

Shigella
Carrying resistance-transfer factors (RTF)   029

Streptomyces coelicolor
Limited mutant stocks for conjugal crosses   030

Vibrio cholerae
P^+ and P^- mutant strains for conjugation experiments   031

Enterobacter & Klebsiella
A wide range of auxotrophs, and mutants blocked in carbohydrate
    metabolism and nitrate reduction   032

Bacteriophages

Virulent

T-series.
T1, wild type   201
T2, wild type   202
T2, mutants, host-range, 'amber', temperature-sensitive (*ts*)   203
T3, wild type   204
T4, wild type   205
T4, mutants: *r*II-point   206
           *r*II-deletion   207
           temperature-sensitive (*ts*).   208
           'amber'   209
           host-range   210
           lysozymeless   211
T5, wild type   212
T6, wild type   213
T7, wild type   214

Others
Single-stranded DNA (ϕX174,S13)   215
Sex-specific:
RNA-containing, male-specific, *E.coli*(f2,μ2,MS2)   216
DNA-containing, male-specific, *E.coli*(f1,M13)   217
quasi-specific for female *E.coli*(ϕ2)   218
quasi-specific for *Salmonella*(SP6)   219

Bacteriophages (*cont.*)	Catalogue number

Temperate

λ wild type; restricted transduction of *gal* region in *E.coli*K12 — 220

λ mutants, various — 221

Lysogens for λ suppressor mutants, λ*sus*: permissive and non-permissive hosts for *sus* mutants — 222

λ*dg*, *gal*-transducing, defective strains carrying various lengths of DNA — 223

P1*k*, wild type; generalized transduction in *E.coli* K12 — 224

P1*bc* and P1*bt*; generalized transduction in *E.coli* B/r — 225

P1 mutants — 226

P2, wild type — 227

P22; generalized transduction in *Salmonella* — 228

φ80 (Matsushiro); restricted transduction of tryptophan region in *E.coli* — 229

B.subtilis phages; transducing phages — 230

Phages with DNA infectious for competent *B.subtilis* cells — 231

Proteus mirabilis; generalized transducing phage and mutant host strains — 232

Pseudomonas aeruginosa; transducing phages and host strains — 233

Fungi

Ascomycetes; *Podospora anserina* and *Sordaria macrospora.* — 401

Aspergillus — 402

Fusaria — 403

Neurospora — 404

Saccharomyces — 405

Ustilago — 406

See introductory note to Appendix B for abbreviations

GEOGRAPHICAL CLASSIFICATION OF LABORATORIES

1 UNITED KINGDOM AND EIRE

Eire

IR1   Dr G.W.Dawson,
Department of Genetics,
Trinity College,
Dublin.

United Kingdom

UK1   Dr T.W.Burrows,
Microbiological Research Establishment,
Porton,
nr. Salisbury, Wiltshire.

UK2   Professor J.R.Fincham,
Department of Genetics,
The University,
Leeds, Yorkshire.

UK3   Professor W.Hayes,
Department of Molecular Biology,
University of Edinburgh,
West Mains Road, Edinburgh, 9.

UK4   Dr D.A.Hopwood,
School of Biological Sciences,
University of East Anglia,
Norwich

UK5   Dr B.W.Bainbridge,
Microbiology Department,
Queen Elizabeth College,
(University of London)
Sir John Atkins Laboratories,
Campden Hill, London, W.8.

UK6   Professor R.H.Pritchard,
Department of Genetics,
The University,
Leicester.

UK7   Dr K.A.Stacey,
School of Biological Sciences,
University of Sussex,
Falmer, Brighton, Sussex.

UK8   Professor N.Symonds,
School of Biological Sciences,
University of Sussex,
Falmer, Brighton, Sussex.

UK9   Dr R.Holliday,
National Institute for Medical Research,
Mill Hill,
London, N.W.7.

UK10   Dr R.F.O.Kemp,
Department of Zoology,
University College,
Swansea, Glam.

2 WESTERN EUROPE

Belgium

BE1   Professor J.Beumer,
Institut Pasteur du Brabant,
Rue de Rémorqueur 28,
Bruxelles.

BE2   Professor P. Frédéricq,
Service de Microbiologie et Hygiène,
Université de Liège,
1 Rue des Bonnes-Villes, Liège.

BE3   Professor R.Thomas,
Laboratoire de Génétique,
Université Libre de Bruxelles,
67, Paardestraat, St. Genesius-Rode.

Denmark

DE1   Dr O.Maaløe,
Universitetets Mikrobiologiske Institut,
Øster Farimagsgade 2A,
Copenhagen K.

Finland

FI1   Dr Helen Makëla,
Department of Serology and Bacteriology,
University of Helsinki,
Helsinki.

France

FR1   Dr C.Anagnoustopolus,
Laboratoire de Génétique,
C.N.R.S.,
Gif-sur-Yvette (Seine-et-Oise).

FR2   Dr R.Devoret,
Centre des Faibles Radioactivités,
C.N.R.S.,
Gif-sur-Yvette (Seine-et-Oise).

Germany (West)

WG1   Professor K.Esser,
Institut für allgemeine Botanik,
Ruhr Universität,
Bochum.

WG2   Dr P.H.Hofschneider,
Max-Planck-Institut für Biochemie,
Goethestrasse 31,
8 Munich, 15.

WG3   Professor F.Kaudewitz,
Max-Planck-Institut für vergleichende Erbbiologie
    & Erbpathologie,
Ehrenbergstrasse 26,
1000 Berlin 33.

WG4   Dr P.Starlinger,
Institut für Genetik,
Universität zu Köln,
Weyertal 115, Köln Lindenthal.

WG5   Dr W.Vielmetter,
Max-Planck-Institut für Virusforschung,
Spemannstrasse 35/1,
Tübingen.

Greece

GR1   Dr Polixeni Kontomichalou,
Department of Bacteriology,
University of Athens,
19 Academias Street, Athens.

GR2   Professor J.Papavassiliou,
Department of Microbiology,
University of Athens,
Goudi-Ampelokipi, Athens.

Israel

IS1   Dr A.Keynan,
National Council for Research & Development,
P.O.Box 20125, 84 Hachashmonaim Street,
Tel Aviv.

Italy

IT1   Dr E.Calef,
Laboratorio Internazionale di Genetica e
    Biofisica,
Via Claudio 1,
Napoli.

IT2   Professor G.A.Maccacaro,
Istituto di Microbiologia,
Via Mangiagelli 31,
Milano.

IT3   Professor G.Sermonti,
Istituto Superiore di Sanita,
Viale Regina Elena 299,
Roma.

Netherlands

NE1   Professor P.G.de Haan,
Laboratorium voor Microbiologie,
Rijksuniversiteit,
Catherijnesingel, 59, Utrecht.

NE2   Dr A.Rörsch,
Medisch Biologisch Laboratorium RVO TNO,
Lange Kleiweg 139,
Rijswijk Z.H.

NE3   Dr A.H.Stouthamer,
        Vrije Universiteit,
        Zoologisch Laboratorium,
        de Boelelaan 1087,
        Amsterdam.

        Norway
NO1   Professor S.Laland,
        Biokjemisk Institutt,
        Universitetet i Oslo,
        Blindern.

        Spain
SP1   Dr V.Sanchis-Bayarri Vaillant,
        Cathedratico de Higiene y Microbiologia,
        Facultad de Medicina,
        Avenida Marques de Sotelo, 11,
        Valencia, 2.

        Sweden
SW1   Dr G.Bertani
        Department of Microbial Genetics,
        Karolinska Institutet,
        Stockholm 60.

        Switzerland
SZ1   Professor U.Leupold,
        Institut für allgemeine Mikrobiologie,
        Universität zu Bern,
        Altenbergrain 21, Bern.

3 SOVIET UNION AND EASTERN EUROPE

        Czechoslovakia
CZ1   Dr M.Kocur (National Collection)
        Department of Microbiology,
        J. E. Purkyne University,
        Kotlarska 2, Brno.

        Germany (East)
EG1   Dr. H.Böhme,
        Institut für Kulturpflanzenforschung,
        Kreis Aschersleben,
        Gatersleben.

EG2   Professor E.Geissler,
       Institut für Mikrobiologie,
       Universität zu Rostock,
       Rostock.

EG3   Dr. H.Prauser,
       Institut für Mikrobiologie u.exp.Therapie,
       Beuthenbergstrasse 11,
       Jena.

Hungary

HU1   Professor G.Ivanovics,
       Department of Microbiology,
       Medical University,
       Szeged.

Poland

PO1   Professor Z.Buchzowski,
       Institute of Marine Medicine,
       Ul. Hibnera 1 c,
       Gdansk-Wrzeszcz.

PO2   Dr Z.Kwiatkowski,
       Institute of Microbiology,
       University of Warsaw,
       Warsaw.

PO3   Dr T.Lachowicz,
       Department of Microbial Genetics,
       Institute of Immunology,
       Chalubinskigo 4, Wroclaw.

PO4   Professor Z.Lowkiewicz,
       Department of General Microbiology,
       The University Akademicka,
       Lublin 14.

PO5   Dr Alexandra Putrament,
       Department of Genetics,
       The University,
       Warsaw.

Rumania

RU1   Professor N.Nestorescu,
       Institutul de Microbiologie, Parazitologie &
           Epidemiologie,
       'Dr I.Cantacuzino', Spl. Independentei 103,
       Bucuresti.

Soviet Union

SU1   Professor D.Goldfarb
       Institute of Genetics,
       USSR Academy of Sciences,
       Profsoyuznaya 7,
       Moscow B-133.

SU2   Dr V.N.Kouznetzova,
       Gamaleya Institute for Epidemiology &
           Microbiology
       Gamaleya Street 2,
       Moscow.

SU3   Dr C.Kvitko,
       Department of Genetics,
       University of Leningrad,
       Leningrad.

SU4   Dr A.Pekhov,
       Institute of Experimental Biology,
       Academy of Medical Sciences,
       8 Baltijskiy Street, Moscow.

SU5   Dr V.P.Shipkov,
       Institute of Experimental Biology,
       Academy of Medical Sciences,
       8 Baltijskiy Street, Moscow.

Yugoslavia

YU1   Dr Vera Zgaga,
       Institut 'Ruder Boskovic',
       Bijenicka, 56,
       Zagreb.

4 NORTH AMERICA

Canada

CA1   Dr Etta Käfer-Boothroyd,
       Department of Genetics,
       McGill University,
       Montreal, P.Q.

CA2   Dr I.Takahashi,
       Biology Department,
       McMaster University,
       Hamilton, Ontario.

CA3   Dr K.E.Sanderson,
          Department of Biology,
          University of Calgary
          Calgary, Alberta.

          United States
US1   Dr E.A.Adelberg,
          Department of Microbiology,
          Yale University,
          310 Cedar Street
          New Haven, Connecticut, 06510.

US2   Dr L.Baron,
          Division of Immunology
          Walter Reed Army Institute of Research,
          Washington D.C., 20012.

US3   Dr Martha Baylor,
          Marine Biology Laboratory,
          Woods Hole, Massachusetts, 02543.

US4   Dr A.Campbell,
          Department of Biology,
          University of Rochester,
          Rochester, N.Y., 14627.

US5   Dr S.Champe,
          Department of Biological Sciences,
          Purdue University,
          Lafayette, Indiana, 47907.

US6   Dr A.J.Clark,
          Department of Bacteriology,
          University of California,
          Berkeley, California, 94720.

US7   Dr R.C.Clowes,
          Division of Biology,
          Southwest Center for Advanced Studies,
          P.O.Box 30365
          Dallas, Texas, 75230.

US8   Dr R.Curtiss,
          Biology Division,
          Oak Ridge National Laboratory,
          Oak Ridge, Tennessee, 37831.

US10 Dr F.J.de Serres
Biology Division
Oak Ridge National Laboratory,
Oak Ridge, Tennessee, 37831.

US11 Dr R.S.Edgar,
Biology Division
California Institute of Technology,
Pasadena, California, 91109.

US12 Dr E.Englesberg,
Dept. of Biological Sciences,
University of California,
Santa Barbara, California, 92706.

US13 Dr P.E.Hartman,
Mergenthaler Laboratory for Biology,
Johns Hopkins University,
Baltimore, Maryland, 21218.

US14 Dr A.D.Kaiser,
Department of Biochemistry
Stanford University,
Stanford, California, 94305.

US15 Professor C.C.Lindegren,
Biological Research Laboratory,
Southern Illinois University,
Carbondale, Illinois, 62901.

US16 Dr S.E.Luria,
Department of Biology,
Massachusetts Institute of Technology,
Cambridge, Massachusetts, 02139.

US17 Dr P.Margolin,
Biological Laboratory,
Long Island Biological Association,
Cold Spring Harbor, Long Island, N.Y., 11724.

US18 Dr Thomas Matney,
M.D.Anderson Hospital,
Texas Medical Center,
Houston, Texas, 77025.

US19 Dr M.Meselson,
Biological Laboratories,
Harvard University,
Cambridge, Massachusetts, 02138.

US20   Dr R.K.Mortimer,
        Donner Laboratory,
        University of California,
        Berkeley, California, 94720.

US21   Dr D.Perkins,
        Department of Biological Sciences,
        Stanford University,
        Stanford, California, 94305.

US22   Dr G.Streisinger,
        Institute of Molecular Biology,
        University of Oregon,
        Eugene, Oregon, 97403.

US23   Dr V. Woodward
        Department of Genetics
        University of Minnesota
        Minneapolis, Minnesota, 55455

US24   Dr C.Yanofsky,
        Biology Department,
        Stanford University,
        Stanford, California, 94305.

US25   Dr N.D.Zinder,
        Rockefeller Institute for Medical Research,
        66th Street & York Avenue,
        New York, N.Y., 10021.

US26   Fungal Genetics Stock Center,
        Department of Biological Sciences,
        Dartmouth College,
        Hanover, New Hampshire, 03755.

5 INDIA

India

IN1   Dr K.Bhaskaran,
        Central Drug Research Institute,
        Lucknow.

IN2   Dr O.Siddiqi,
        Tata Institute of Fundamental Research,
        Colaba, Bombay 5.

6 JAPAN

Japan

JA1   Dr T.Iino,
        Department of Microbial Genetics,
        National Institute of Genetics,
        Yata 1, 111, Misima, Sizuoka-ken.

JA2   Dr Y.Hirota,
        Department of Genetics,
        University of Osaka,
        Osaka.

JA3   Dr J.Tomizawa,
        National Institute of Health,
        Shinagawa-Ku,
        Tokyo.

JA4   Dr T.Watanabe,
        Department of Bacteriology,
        Keio University,
        Tokyo.

7 AUSTRALASIA

Australia

AU1   Professor D.G.Catcheside
        Department of Genetics,
        John Curtin School of Medical Research,
        Australian National University, Canberra.

AU2   Dr B.Holloway,
        Department of Genetics,
        Monash University,
        P.O. Box 92,
        Clayton, Victoria.

AU3   Dr P.Reeves,
        Department of Microbiology,
        The University,
        Adelaide.

New Zealand

NZ1   Dr P.Bergquist,
        Microbiology Department,
        University of Auckland,
        P.O.Box 2175,
        Auckland.

NZ2   Dr Sheila Howarth (Thompson),
        Microbiology Department,
        P.O.Box 913,
        University of Otago,
        Dunedin.

NZ3   Dr Barbara Segedin,
        Botany Department,
        University of Auckland,
        P.O.Box 2175,
        Auckland.

8 AFRICA

United Arab Republic

UA1   Dr A.M.M.Ali,
        National Research Centre,
        Genetics Unit,
        Dokki, Cairo.

DOCUMENT III

BACTERIA

Catalogue No. of Strain	Geographical Region							
	1	2	3	4	5	6	7	8
001	UK_3 UK_7	FR_1 GR_1 WG_2 GR_2 WG_3 NE_2 WG_4 IT_2	EG_2 RU_1 EG_3 SU_4 HU_1 SU_5 PO_1	CA_2 US_2 US_7 US_{10}	IN_1 IN_2	JA_2	AU_3	UA_1
002			HU_1	CA_2				
003			HU_1					
004	UK_3 UK_6	BE_2 GR_2 F_1 IS_1 FR_2 IT_1 WG_2 IT_2 WG_3 NE_1 WG_4 NE_2 WG_5 NO_1 GR_1 SP_1 SW_1	CZ_1 SU_1 EG_1 SU_2 EG_2 SU_4 EG_3 SU_5 HU_1 YU_1 PO_1 PO_2 RU_1	CA_2 US_{13} US_1 US_{16} US_2 US_{18} US_7 US_{25} US_8 US_{10} US_{12}	IN_1 IN_2	JA_1 JA_2 JA_4	AU_2 AU_3 NZ_2	UA_1
005	UK_3 UK_7	BE_2 IS_1 F_1 IT_1 FR_2 IT_2 WG_2 NE_1 WG_3 NE_2 WG_4 NO_1 WG_5 SW_1 GR_2	EG_1 SU_5 EG_2 HU_1 PO_1 PO_2 RU_1 SU_1 SU_4	US_1 US_{18} US_2 US_{25} US_6 CA_2 US_7 US_8 US_{10} US_{12} US_{16}	IN_1 IN_2	JA_1 JA_2 JA_4	AU_2 AU_3	

No.	UK	Europe	HU/PO/RU...	US	IN/US12	JA	AU	UA
006	UK3	BE2 FR2 GR1 GR2 IT1 NO1 SW1	HU1 PO1 PO4 RU1	US2 US7 US10		JA1 JA2 JA4	AU2 AU3 NZ2	UA1
007	UK3	BE2 GR1 GR2 IT1 NO1 SW1	HU1 PO1 PO4 RU1	US2 US7 US18		JA1 JA2 JA4	AU2	
008	UK3							
009		FR2 NE2*		US8				
010				US8				
011	UK3	BE1 BE2 FI1 WG2 WG3 WG4 WG5 GR1 GR2 IT1 IT2 NE1 NE2 NO1 SW1	CZ1 PO1 RU1 SU1 SU2 SU4 SU5 YU1	US2 US7 US8 US10 US12 US13 US16 US18 US25	IN2	JA1 JA2 JA4	AU2 AU3	
012					US12			
013		BE2 FI1 WG2 WG3 WG4 WG5 GR1 GR2 IT1 IT2 NE1 NE2 SW1	CZ1 PO1 RU1 SU1 SU2 SU4 SU5 YU1	US2 US10 US12 US13 US16 US18 US25		JA1 JA2 JA4	AU2	

BACTERIA

* Wide range of temperature-sensitive mutants available.

BACTERIA

Catalogue No. of Strain	Geographical Region							
	1	2	3	4	5	6	7	8
014		SW1						
015			EG3					
016	UK6, UK7	DE1, FR2, WG2, WG3, WG4, WG5, GR1, GR2, IT1, NE1, NE2, NO1	EG2, EG3, PO1, RU1, SU1, SU2, SU4, SU5, YU1	US1, US2, US10, US18	IN2	JA2	AU2, AU3	UA1
017		DE1	YU1					
018		GR1		US18				
019	UK1							
020				US2				
021			EG1					
022			CZ1				AU2, NZ2	

	BACTERIA							
	IR1 UK3	FI1 GR1 WG3 GR2 WG4 IT2 WG5	PO1 RU1	CA3 US12 US2 US13 US7 US17 US10 US18	IN1	JA1 JA2 JA4	AU2 NZ2	UA1
023	IR1 UK3	FI1 GR1 WG3 GR2 WG4 IT2 WG5	PO1 RU1	CA3 US12 US2 US13 US7 US17 US10 US18	IN1	JA1 JA2 JA4	AU2 NZ2	UA1
024				CA3 US13†				
025		FI1		CA3				
026		BE2 GR2 FI1 IT1 GR1	PO1	US2 US13 US7 US18 US10	IN1	JA1 JA2 JA4	AU2	
027		FI1 GR2 GR1 IT2	PO1	US2 US13 US10	IN1	JA1 JA2 JA4	AU2	
028				US2				
029						JA4		
030	UK4	IT3						
031					IN1			
032		NE3						

† Especially histidineless (*his*) mutants.

BACTERIOPHAGES

Catalogue No. of Strain	Geographical Region							
	1	2	3	4	5	6	7	8
201	UK8	BE1 WG5 BE2 IT1 FR2 IT2 WG2 NE1 WG3 NE2 WG4 IS1	CZ1 EG3 PO1 RU1	US2 US7 US8 US10 US16		JA2 JA3 JA4	AU2 AU3	UA1
202	UK8	BE1 IT1 BE2 IT2 FR2 NE1 WG2 NE2 WG3 IS1 WG4 NO1 WG5	CZ1 EG3 PO1 RU1 SU1 SU2	US2 US7 US8 US9 US10 US16		JA2 JA3 JA4	AU2 AU3 NZ1	UA1
203			SU1	US3				
204	UK8	BE1 WG5 BE2 IT1 FR2 IT2 WG2 NE1 WG3 NE2 WG4 IS1	CZ1 EG3 PO1 RU1	US2 US7 US8 US10 US16		JA2 JA3 JA4	AU2 AU3	UA1

205	UK8	BE1 WG5 BE2 IS1 GR1 IT1 GR2 IT2 WG2 NE1 WG3 NE2 WG4	CZ1 EG3 PO1 RU1	US2 US7 US8 US10 US16 US18	IN2	JA2 JA3 JA4	AU2 AU3	UA1
206	UK8	WG2 IT1 WG4 NE2 GR1 GR2	HU1 PO1 RU1 YU1	US5* US13 US7 US16 US10 US11†	IN2	JA2 JA3	AU2 NZ1	UA1
207	UK8	WG2 IT1 WG4 GR1 GR2	HU1 PO1 RU1 YU1	US5* US11† US7 US13 US10 US16	IN2	JA3	AU2 NZ1	UA1
208		WG2 IT1	HU1 PO1	US11†	IN2	JA3	AU2	
209		WG2 IT1 WG4	HU1 PO1	US11†	IN2	JA3	AU2	
210		WG2 GR2 WG4 IT1 GR1	HU1 PO1	US7 US11† US10 US13	IN2	JA3	AU2	
211				US22				
212	UK8	BE1 WG5 BE2 IS1 WG2 IT1 WG3 IT2 WG4 NE1	CZ1 EG3 PO1 RU1 SU2	US2 US7 US8 US10 US16		JA2 JA3 JA4	AU2 AU3 NZ1	UA1

* To be requested by *original* published numbers only (Benzer).
† World distribution.

BACTERIOPHAGES

Catalogue No. of Strain	Geographical Region							
	1	2	3	4	5	6	7	8
213	UK8	BE1 WG5 BE2 IS1 FR2 IT1 WG2 IT2 WG3 NO1 WG4 NE1	CZ1 EG3 PO1 RU1	US2 US7 US8 US10 US16 US18	IN2	JA2 JA3 JA4	AU2 AU3 NZ1	UA1
214	UK8	BE1 WG5 BE2 IS1 WG2 IT1 WG3 IT2 WG4 NE1	CZ1 EG3 PO1 RU1	US2 US7 US8 US10		JA2 JA3 JA4	AU2 AU3 NZ1	UA1
215		WG2 IT1 WG5 NE1 IS1 NE2	EG2 PO1 SU2	US2 US25 US10 US25	IN2	JA2 JA3	AU2 AU3	
216	UK3	FR2 IS1 WG2 IT1 WG3 IT2 WG5 NE1 GR1 NE2 GR2	PO1 RU1 SU1 SU2 SU4 SU5	US2 US25 US6 US7 US8 US10 US18	IN1 IN2	JA2 JA3 JA4	AU2 AU3 NZ1	UA1
217		WG2						
218	UK3	IT2						
219				US25				

BACTERIOPHAGES

220	UK3	BE2 GR2, BE3 IT1, FR2 IT2, WG2 NE2, WG3 NO1, WG4 SW1, GR1	EG2, EG3, PO1, RU1, SU1, SU2, SU4	US2 US18, US6 US19, US7 US25, US8, US10, US14, US16	IN2	JA2, JA3, JA4	AU2, AU3, NZ1	UA1
221		WG2 SW1, WG3, WG4, IT1, NE2, BE3	EG2 SU2, EG3 SU4, PO1, RU1, SU1	US2 US16, US7 US18, US8 US19, US10 US25, US14, US4*	IN2	JA2, JA3, JA4	AU2, NZ1	
222				US4				
223								
224	UK3	BE2 IT1, WG3 IT2, WG4 NE1, WG5 SW1, GR1, GR2	PO1, RU1	US2 US14, US6 US16, US7 US18, US8 US19, US10 US25, US13	IN2	JA2, JA3, JA4	AU2, AU3	UA1
225				US12				
226		WG3, WG4, WG5, IT1, SW1	PO1, RU1	US2 US14, US7 US16, US8 US18, US10 US19, US13 US25		JA2, JA3, JA4	AU2	
227		WG3 IT1, GR1 IT2, GR2 SW1	PO1	US2 US25, US10, US18		JA3		

* Complete set of λ sus mutants, 1–128, available.

	Catalogue No. of Strain	Geographical Region							
		1	2	3	4	5	6	7	8
BACTERIOPHAGES	228	UK3	WG3 GR2 WG4 IT1 WG5 IT2 GR1 SW1	PO1 RU1	US2 US13 US7 US18 US8 US25 US10		JA2 JA3 JA4	AU2	UA1
	229				US2				
	230			EG2 HU1	CA2				
	231			HU1					
	232			EG1					
	233		WG1	CZ1					
FUNGI	401							AU2	
	402	UK5 UK6	WG1 IS1 IT1	PO2 PO5	US26* CA1	IN2		NZ3	UA1
	403								UA1
	404	UK2	WG3		US23 US26*			AU1 NZ1	UA1
	405	UK10	SZ1	PO3	US15* US20				UA1
	406	UK9			US26				UA1

* World distribution.

Appendix D
Genealogy of some common *E.coli* K12 strains

The two family trees on the following pages are compiled from information gathered from many laboratories and individuals. They are the 'best guess' for the derivation of these strains, but there are undoubtedly many errors and they should be taken only as a rough guide.
The original K12 ('wild-type') parental strain grows on a simple medium of inorganic salts plus glucose (the 'minimal medium' e.g. Appendix A6 or A7) and requires no other growth supplement. This type of growth is referred to as 'prototrophic'. Mutants requiring accessory growth factors are termed 'auxotrophic'.
Much of the information shown in these pedigrees came from the laboratory of Dr J.Lederberg and was made available by Dr Helen Bernstein.
For an explanation of symbols: see Appendix B, p.193.

1. thr⁻leu⁻thi⁻ strains

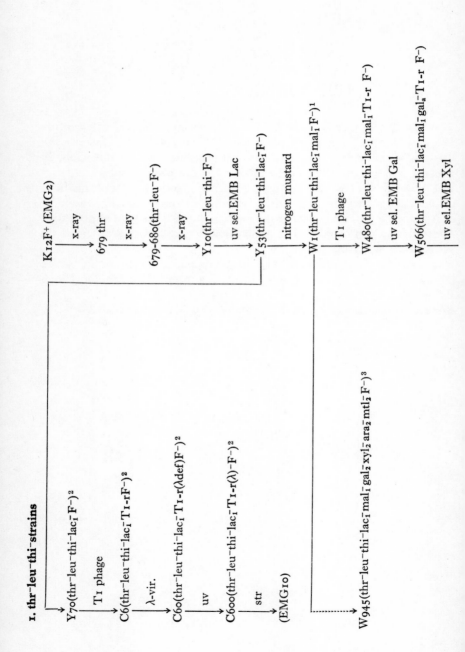

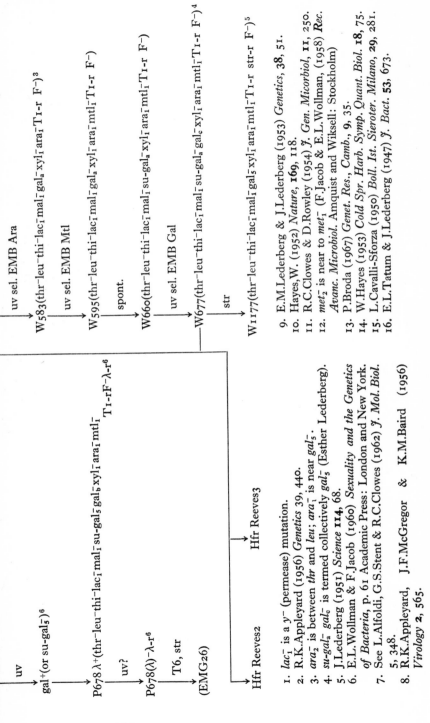

uv

gal⁺(or su-gal₅⁻)[6]

P678λ⁺(thr⁻leu⁻thi⁻lac₁⁻mal₁⁻su-gal₅⁻gal_b⁻xyl₁⁻ara₁⁻mtl₁⁻ T1-rF⁻λ-r⁶)

uv?

P678(λ)-λ-r⁶

T6, str

(EMG26)

uv sel. EMB Ara

W583(thr⁻leu⁻thi⁻lac₁⁻mal₁⁻gal_a⁻xyl₁⁻ara₁⁻T1-r F⁻)[3]

uv sel. EMB Mtl

W595(thr⁻leu⁻thi⁻lac₁⁻mal₁⁻gal_a⁻xyl₁⁻ara₁⁻mtl₁⁻T1-r F⁻)

spont.

W660(thr⁻leu⁻thi⁻lac₁⁻mal₁⁻su-gal_a⁻xyl₁⁻ara₁⁻mtl₁⁻T1-r F⁻)

uv sel. EMB Gal

W677(thr⁻leu⁻thi⁻lac₁⁻mal₁⁻su-gal_a⁻gal_c⁻xyl₁⁻ara₁⁻mtl₁⁻T1-r F⁻)[4]

str

W1177(thr⁻leu⁻thi⁻lac₁⁻mal₁⁻gal₅⁻xyl₁⁻ara₁⁻mtl₁⁻T1-r str-r F⁻)[5]

→ Hfr Reeves2

→ Hfr Reeves3

1. lac₁⁻ is a y⁻ (permease) mutation.
2. R.K.Appleyard (1956) Genetics 39, 440.
3. ara₂⁻ is between thr and leu; ara₁⁻ is near gal₅⁻.
4. su-gal_a⁻ gal_c⁻ is termed collectively gal₅⁻ (Esther Lederberg).
5. J.Lederberg (1951) Science 114, 68.
6. E.L.Wollman & F.Jacob (1960) Sexuality and the Genetics of Bacteria, p. 61 Academic Press: London and New York.
7. See L.Alfoldi, G.S.Stent & R.C.Clowes (1962) J. Mol. Biol. 5, 348.
8. R.K.Appleyard, J.F.McGregor & K.M.Baird (1956) Virology 2, 565.
9. E.M.Lederberg & J.Lederberg (1953) Genetics, 38, 51.
10. Hayes,W. (1952) Nature, 169, 118.
11. R.C.Clowes & D.Rowley (1954) J. Gen. Microbiol, 11, 250.
12. met₂⁻ is near to met₁⁻ (F.Jacob & E.L.Wollman, (1958) Rec. Avanc. Microbiol. Amquist and Wiksell: Stockholm)
13. P.Broda (1967) Genet. Res., Camb., 9, 35.
14. W.Hayes (1953) Cold Spr. Harb. Symp. Quant. Biol. 18, 75.
15. L.Cavalli-Sforza (1950) Boll. Ist. Sieroter. Milano, 29, 281.
16. E.L.Tatum & J.Lederberg (1947) J. Bact. 53, 673.

2. met⁻ and other strains

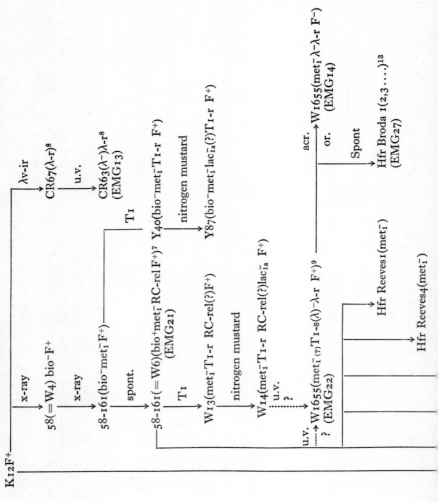

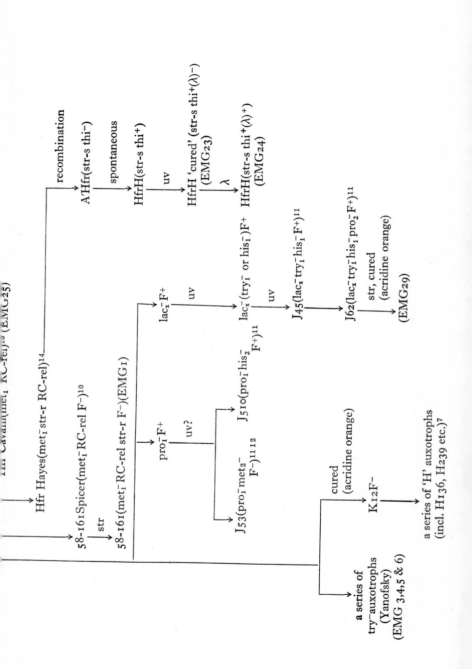

III Cavalli(met₁⁻ RC-rel)¹⁹ (EMG25)

→ Hfr Hayes(met₁⁻ str-r RC-rel)¹⁴

recombination

A'Hfr(str-s thi⁻)

spontaneous

HfrH(str-s thi⁺)

uv

HfrH 'cured' (str-s thi⁺(λ))⁻ (EMG23)

λ

HfrH(str-s thi⁺(λ))⁺ (EMG24)

58-161Spicer(met₁⁻ RC-rel F⁻)¹⁰

str

58-161(met₁⁻ RC-rel str-r F⁻)(EMG1)

pro₁⁻ F⁺

uv?

J510(pro₁⁻his₂⁻ F⁺)¹¹

J53(pro₁⁻met₂⁻ F⁻)¹¹²

lac_x⁻ F⁺

uv

lac_x⁻(try₁⁻ or his₁⁻)F⁺

uv

J45(lac_x⁻try₁⁻his₁⁻F⁺)¹¹

J62(lac_x⁻try₁⁻his₁⁻pro₂⁻F⁺)¹¹

str, cured (acridine orange) (EMG29)

cured (acridine orange)

K12F⁻

a series of 'H' auxotrophs (incl. H136, H239 etc.)⁷

a series of try⁻auxotrophs (Yanofsky) (EMG 3,4,5 & 6)

227

Appendix E
Amino acid, vitamins and purine/pyrimidine pools used in the determination of auxotrophic requirements
(after R. Holliday (1956) *Nature*, **178**, 1987)††

The growth factors shown in the table below are each made up aseptically in sterile distilled water at the concentrations indicated. They are then combined aseptically in equal volumes to form the pools shown in the vertical columns 1 to 6, and in different combinations to form the pools 7 to 12 as shown by the horizontal columns, and stored at 4°. They may now be added to liquid minimal medium or to minimal agar (1 ml pool per 100 ml medium). Any single growth-factor requirement will show as growth on two of the 12 pools only, e.g., a *try*-requiring auxotroph will grow only on pools 3 and 9. Growth on one pool only indicates a requirement for two or more factors in the pool. Growth on more than two pools indicates an alternative requirement e.g. growth on pools 3, 6, and 8 would be shown by a mutant requiring *either* serine *or* glycine.

Pool	1	2	3	4	5	6
7	adenine †	biotin‡ (1)	phenyl-alanine*	alanine*	arginine*	leucine*
8	hypoxanthine†	folic acid‡ (50)	serine*	cysteine*	ornithine*	glycine*
9	cytosine †	pantothenic acid‡ (50)	tryptophan*	threonine*	aspartic acid*	isoleucine*
10	guanine †	pyridoxin‡ (50)	tyrosine*	sodium thiosulphate†	proline*	histidine*
11	thymine †	thiamin‡ (1)	p-amino-benzoic acid‡ (50)	methionine*	glutamic acid*	lysine*
12	uracil†	riboflavin‡ (250)	nicotinic acid‡ (50)	choline‡ (1000)	inositol‡ (500)	valine*

FOOTNOTES: See facing page

Appendix F

Templates (Expts. 2 and 29)

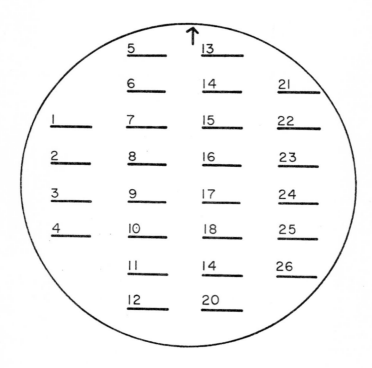

Appendix G

(see p.26)

The value of aNt as a function of r for various values of C (r from 0.1 to 10)

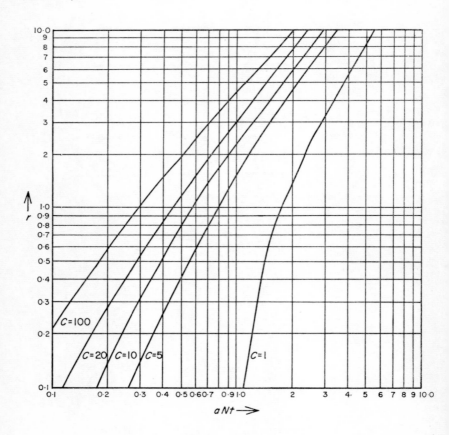

The value of aNt as a function of r for various values of C (r from 0.1 to 100)

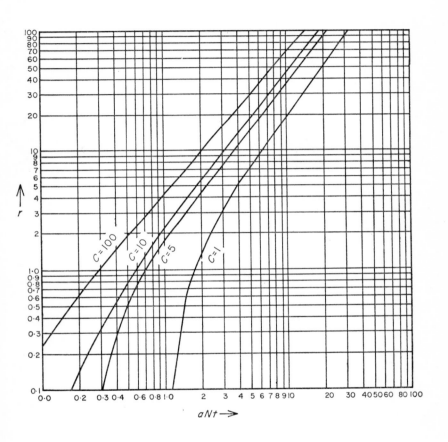

Appendix H
Preparation of antiphage sera

This can be conveniently produced by the immunization of rabbits. The phage stock should have at least 10^{10} pfu/ml and may be used as a crude, broth lysate that has been previously centrifuged and filtered to remove bacteria and debris. The animal is conveniently injected either intravenously (5 ml into the marginal ear vein is a common procedure when high titre stocks are used) although the subcutaneous route is probably much simpler (20 ml of a lower titre stock can readily be injected into the interscapular space). Usually two injections per week over a three-week period are adequate, although a 'booster' injection, two weeks after the termination of the first course will usually increase the final titre. The animal is then bled, usually one week after the last injection (a test-bleeding of 2 or 3 ml is first taken from the marginal ear vein and assayed as below). Final bleeding may be either from the ear as above, by cardiac puncture, or by femoral bleeding of an ether-anaesthetized animal followed by killing. The blood is allowed to clot at 37° and refrigerated overnight. The red cells are then removed by low-speed centrifugation and the serum is filtered through a membrane filter and preserved aseptically.

Determination of K value of anti-serum

Phage particles are inactivated by their specific antiserum in an exponential manner, as expressed in the equation:

$$c = c_o e^{-Kt}$$

where c = phage concentration after antiserum treatment.
c_o = original phage concentration
t = time in minutes
K = constant

The strength of any particular phage antiserum can thus be expressed in terms of the constant (K). However, since antisera are usually employed at some dilution (D) of their original strength, this equation may be rewritten as:

$$K = 2.3 \frac{D}{t} \log \frac{c_o}{c}$$

where the logarithm is now to the base 10, and the equation refers to the diluted antiserum used in a particular tube.

Phage antisera prepared as above, may have K values ranging from 10 to over 1000, depending on the phage used and other variables operating during the course of the inoculation and bleeding.

An easy way of obtaining a rough K value of an antiserum is as follows:

Dilute the antiserum three-fold in broth and repeat this three-fold dilution into a further four tubes, to produce a series of dilutions ranging from 0 through 3,9,27 and 81 to 243. Take 0.1 ml from each dilution into a small test-tube. Then proceed as follows according to the time schedule:

Time (min)

0	Add 0.9 ml of the relevant phage at 1×10^6/ml to the tube containing the undiluted antiserum.
1	Add 0.9 ml of the same phage suspension to the tube containing the first dilution of the antiserum.
2,3,4 and 5	Repeat with subsequent antiserum dilutions.
6	Take 0.1 ml from $t = 0$ tube into 0.9 ml buffer (to stop the reaction) and immediately overlay 0.1 ml of this in soft agar on nutrient plates in the presence of the indicator bacteria.
7,8,9,10,11	Repeat the dilution and plating process with other tubes.
15	Incubate all plates overnight.

The next morning one of the plates should contain about 100 phage plaques, *i.e.* the antiserum at that dilution will have reduced the phage titre roughly a hundred-fold. Using the second equation, the approximate K values of the antiserum can be calculated and a more accurate value can then be determined in a more precise experiment of a similar type.

Appendix I
Template (Expt.28)

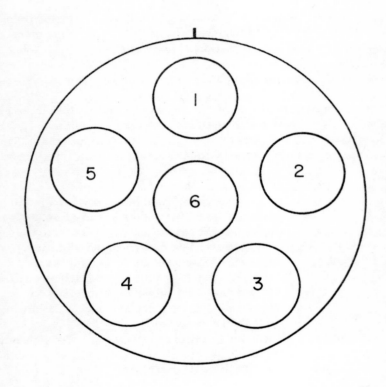

Appendix J
Aspergillus notes

1. Tungsten wire needles

Tungsten wire (cleaned and annealed—0.012 inch diameter) is obtainable from Johnson, Matthey & Co. Ltd., 73 Hatton Garden, London, E.C.1. Extremely fine-pointed needles are made by dipping end of wire into molten $NaNO_2$ until end has been eroded to fine point.

2. Wire replicators

Cut out two squares (10 cm) of Perspex or plexiglass (2 mm thick) and cut off corners (1.5 cm). Drill one square with 33 holes to take steel dress-making pins and ensure a tight fit, countersinking to accommodate head. Holes should be in form of a 5 cm × 5 cm square with an additional 8 holes outside the square so as to make full use of the area available on a circular petri dish. After inserting pins, the second square is stuck on top with chloroform to hold pins in place. A template of cardboard for marking dishes can easily be made, viz.:

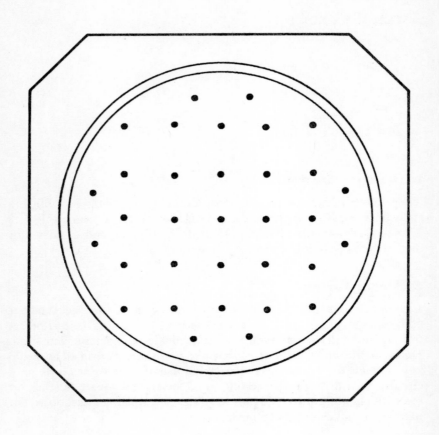

Appendix K
Electronic circuit for plaque and colony counter

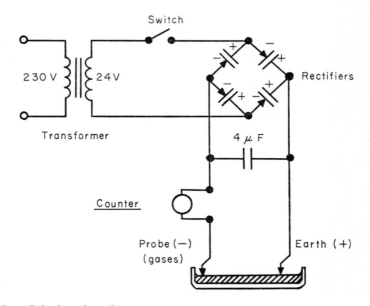

Rectifiers: Selenium 65 mA
Transformer: Single filament 24 v
Counter: 'Sodeco' Impulse Counter 24 v D.C. (TCeZ4E)

A commercial apparatus is available (see p.241).

Appendix L
List of commercial supply houses

Supply Houses (U.K.)

1 *Rotor* (Matburn blood cell suspension mixers, 240 v, 50 cycles)
   Originally made by
   Matburn Ltd.,
   25 Red Lion Street,
   London W.C.1.

   now taken over by
   Magnavox Company Ltd.,
   Alfred's Way, By-Pass Road,
   Barking, Essex.

2 *Petroff-Hauser counting chambers*
   Arnold R. Horwell Ltd.,
   2 Grange Way, Kilburn High Road,
   London, N.W.6.

3 *Whirlimix* (Whirlimixers WM/250)
   Fisons Scientific Apparatus Ltd.,
   Loughborough, Leicestershire.

4 *Microid shaker*
   Baird and Tatlock Ltd.,
   Freshwater Road,
   Chadwell Heath, Essex.

5 *Hand-tally counter*
   Griffen and George, Ltd.,
   Ealing Road,
   Alperton,
   Wembley, Middlesex.

6   *Electronic counter* ('*Sodeco*'—*Geneva*)
                    Stonebridge Electrical Co.,
                    6 Queen Anne's Gate,
                    London, S.W.1.

7   *Aeration pump* (piston pump type)
                    Medcalf Brothers, Ltd.,
                    Cranborne Industrial Estate,
                    Cranborne Road, Potters Bar, Middlesex.

8   *Valves and manifolds* for above (airline regulator valves)
                    Medcalf Brothers, Ltd.,
                    (See 7 above).

9   *U.V. lamps* (Hanovia model 12 and model 6A UV lamps)
                    Engelhard-Hanovia Industries Ltd.,
                    Slough, Bucks.

10 *Screw-capped bottles* (various sizes)
                    United Glass Ltd.,
                    79 Kingston Road, Kingston, Surrey.

                    or
                    Johnsen & Jorgensen Ltd.,
                    Herringham Road, S.E.7.

11 *Membrane filter holders & filters:*
                    Oxoid
                    Oxoid Limited,
                    Southwark Bridge Road,
                    London E.C.4.

                    Millipore
                    Millipore Ltd.,
                    Heron House,
                    109 Wembley Hill Road, Wembley, Middlesex.

                    Schleicher and Schüll
                    V.A.Howe Ltd.,
                    46 Pembridge Road, London W.11.

12 *Pasteur pipettes*
> Arnold R. Horwell Ltd.,
> 2 Grange Way, Kilburn High Road,
> London N.W.6.
> (Distributors)
>
> or direct from
> Harshaw Chemicals, Ltd.,
> Daventry, Northants.

13 *Aluminium caps* (for test tubes)
> Oxoid Ltd.,
> Southwark Bridge Road,
> London E.C.4.

14 *Plastic plates*
> Sterilin Ltd.,
> 9 The Quadrant,
> Richmond, Surrey.

15 *Stab vials* (Trident containers series SNB)
> Camlab (Glass) Ltd.,
> Milton Road,
> Cambridge.

16 *Platinum wire* (10% iridium-platinum wire, 24 s.w.g.)
> Johnson, Matthey & Company Ltd.,
> 78 Hatton Garden,
> London E.C.1.

17 *Media chemicals*
> Oxoid Ltd.,
> Southwark Bridge Road, London E.C.4.
>
> Baird & Tatlock Ltd., (Difco products)
> Freshwater Road,
> Chadwell Heath, Essex.
>
> Thomas Kerfoot Ltd., (sugars)
> Vale of Bardsley, Ashton-u-Lyne, Lancs.
>
> George T. Gurr Ltd., (dyes)
> 136-138 New Kings Road, London S.W.6.
>
> British Drug Houses Ltd., (various)
> Poole, Dorset.

chemicals to be imported can usually be obtained through:
V.A.Howe Ltd.,
46 Pembridge Road, London W.11.

or
Kodak Research Chemicals Ltd.,
Kirkby, Liverpool.

18 *Sephadex*

Pharmacia Fine Chemicals AB,
Uppsala, Sweden

or
Pharmacia (Great Britain) Ltd.,
Paramount House,
75 Uxbridge Road,
Ealing, London W.5.

Supply Houses (U.S.)

1 *Petroff-Hauser counting chambers*
E.H.Sargent & Co.,
4647 West Foster Avenue,
Chicago, Illinois, 60630.

2 *Vortex Genie Mixer* (*Whirlimix*)
Aloe Scientific,
1831 Olive Street,
St. Louis, Mo., 63103.

3 *Burrell Wrist-Action Shaker* (Microid shaker)
New Brunswick Scientific Co.,
1130 Somerset Street,
New Brunswick, N.J., 08903.

4 *Hand-tally counter*
E.H.Sargent & Co.,
(See 1 above).

5 *Electronic counter*—Luminescent Bacterial Colony
Counter Model C-101 (complete apparatus)
New Brunswick Scientific Co.,
(See 3 above).

Sodeco 12 v. D.C. counter
Landis & Gyr, Inc.,
45 W. 45th Street,
New York, New York, 10036.

6 *U.V. lamp*—G.E. 15 watt (G15T) 'Germicidal' low-pressure
mercury resonance lamp
General Electric,
1 River Road,
Schenectady, New York, 12305.

7 *Screw-capped bottles* (various sizes)
Aloe Scientific
(See 2 above).

8 *Membrane filters and holders*
Oxoid
Colab Laboratories, Inc.,
1526 Hallstead,
Chicago Heights, Illinois, 60411.

Millipore
Millipore Filter Corp.,
Box F,
Bedford, Mass., 01730.

Schleicher and Schuell
Schleicher & Schuell,
541 Washington St.,
Keene, New Hampshire, 03431.

9 *Pasteur pipettes*
Bellco Glass Inc.,
P.O.Box B,
Vineland, New Jersey, 08360.

10. *Aluminum caps*
Colab Laboratories, Inc.
(See 8 above).

11 *Plastic plates*
Aloe Scientific
(See 2 above).

12   *Stab vials*

E.H.Sargent & Co.
(See 1 above).

Screwcapped   W.Hillen
8, Habichtweg
Widdersdorf, 5021
West Germany

13   *Platinum wire*

Aloe Scientific
(See 2 above).

14   *Media chemicals*

Agar   Davis Gelatin (NZ Ltd).,
P.O.Box 9542,
Woolston,
Christchurch, New Zealand.

Media and   Colab Laboratories, Inc.
sugars   (See 8 above)
Difco Laboratories,
920 Henry Street,
Detroit, Michigan, 48201.

Dyes   Allied Chemical Co.,
National Aniline Division,
41 Rector Street,
New York, New York, 10006.

Amino acids,   Nutritional Biochemicals,
vitamins, etc.   21010 Miles Avenue,
Cleveland, Ohio, 44128.
Cal Biochem,
3625 Medford Street,
Los Angeles, California, 90063.

Nitroso-   Aldrich Chemical Co.,
guanidine,   2371 N. 30th,
aminopterin   Milwaukee, Wisconsin, 53210.

Penicillin,   Difco Laboratories,
streptomycin,   (See 14—Media and sugars—above).
sulphonamides

15 *Sephadex*

        Pharmacia Fine Chemicals,
        800 Centennial Avenue,
        Piscataway, New Jersey, 08854.

16 *'Touchomatic' burners*

        Hanau Engineering Co.,
        1235 Main TR,
        Buffalo, New York, 14209.